THE ONE
THAT GOT AWAY

THE ONE
THAT GOT AWAY

TED STONE

Western Producer Prairie Books
Saskatoon, Saskatchewan

Cover design and illustration by Warren Clark

Printed and bound in Canada

The publisher acknowledges the support received for this publication from the Canada Council.

Western Producer Prairie Books is a unique publishing venture located in the middle of western Canada and owned by a group of prairie farmers who are members of Saskatchewan Wheat Pool. From the first book in 1954, a reprint of a serial originally carried in the weekly newspaper, *The Western Producer,* to the book before you now, the tradition of providing enjoyable and informative reading for all Canadians is continued.

Canadian Cataloguing in Publication Data

Stone, Ted, 1947–

The one that got away

ISBN 0–88833–339–0

1. Tall tales—Prairie Provinces.   I. Title.

PS8587.T65O54 1990   C813'.54   C90–097111–8
PR9199.3.S86O54 1990

Contents

*To John Borgert for all the years we spent pike fishing
and to
Mark Robison for pointing out that the first liar never has a chance*

Acknowledgements

Ever since the first fish slipped off a hook and the first stag escaped into the forest, people who enjoy wilderness pursuits have enjoyed stories about the outdoors. I've gathered the tales in this book from people across the continent, from friends and relatives, from strangers who have written with a favorite story, from people who have talked to me on various radio call-in shows.

I'm grateful to everyone who has taken the time to tell me a story or two. I especially thank Doug Stone, Don Phillips, Al Jones, George Crighton, Kim and Maggie Calloway, Peter Schroedter, Dell Persson, Ken Paterson, Don and Lynn McCrea of Trapper Don's Lodge, Neil Wright, Dale Garnham, Obbie Paterson, Gary Paulson, Vera Gingras, Charles Freeman, Harry Kellock, Hap Bednarek, Charlie Taylor, Ron Last, Karl Mohr, Shawn, Lois, and Gary Gurke, and everyone at Treeline Lodge. I also thank my wife, Patti, who is responsible for the omission of several crude and tasteless tales from these pages.

The settings and characters in this book are fictional.
Any resemblances to real people or places
are entirely coincidental.

Tales
to Remember

It all started because of the stories. The hunting and fishing too, but it's the stories that got me going on this. Ever since I was a kid, growing up on the farm, I've spent every minute I could outdoors. I learned to fish for rock bass and trout in the creek at home. I shot rabbits every winter, hunted squirrels and ducks every fall. The first money I ever earned came from trapping muskrats and beavers along the creek between here and Mud Lake.

After I left home and started a business of my own, there were a lot of years when I wasn't able to get out in the woods as much as I'd have liked. Oh, I got away whenever I could. I'd always manage a deer hunt in the fall and I'd usually get out for a few weekends of fishing every summer. Maybe even do some rabbit hunting in the winter. And, of course, most years we'd get in a family camping trip. But it wasn't until after I retired that I could do what I wanted in pretty much the same way as when I was a boy.

And that's when I started thinking how important the stories were. You're likely to hear more than a yarn or two on almost any hunting or fishing trip. And there are always a few tales told at home, between trips, too. Sometimes, I even wonder what it is I enjoy more, getting out in the woods or talking about it once I get home.

My trouble is I've got a revolving-door memory. I forget as many stories as I remember. You know what they say about getting old. The first three things you lose are your sight, your hearing, and . . . I seem to have forgotten the other one. I guess that's why I decided

1

to write down all these yarns and tall-tales. I don't want to forget any more of them than I already have.

I started on this project just a couple of weeks after I retired. I'd gone on a fishing trip with my old hunting and fishing buddy Marv Thompson. Marv's as full of what the bull drops as anybody you're ever likely to meet. We've been chasing around together since we were about twelve years old so he's told me more than a few stretchers over the years.

I can remember one time he told me he was the greatest hunter who ever lived. He said all he had to do was walk in the woods and any game within two hundred yards would just lie down and die once it realized such a great hunter was there. Marv said it had got so he didn't even take a gun with him anymore. He said he hadn't needed to shoot a deer in three years. I told him what he meant was that he hadn't *been able* to shoot a deer in three years.

Marv just laughed. He said that he'd gotten a deer every year of his life since he killed his first one with a slingshot back when he was six years old. Well, of course, I knew better than that so I asked him how he managed to kill a deer with a slingshot.

"It was easy," he said. "I tracked the deer for three days and then, when I finally snuck up within about twenty yards of him, I loaded a pebble into my slingshot, aimed for a spot just behind his shoulder, and let her rip. The deer didn't have a chance."

I wasn't about to let Marv get away with that and I interrupted his story to tell him that a pebble shot in a slingshot by a six-year-old boy would never kill a deer. I said I didn't care if it was only twenty yards away, the shot was perfect, and the deer was a hundred years old, a kid's slingshot wouldn't even be able to break the skin.

"Well no, of course not," said Marv. "But since I was only six years old, my aim wasn't as good as it is now. My pebble hit the deer back by his tail and when he jumped up, turning his head to see what stung him, his antlers hit a tree so hard he broke his neck. It was a nice eight-point buck, too. If it hadn't been that one of the points broke off when it hit the tree, I would have gotten the head mounted."

Marv and I were bass fishing the day I got the idea to write this book. It was like most days fishing with Marv. He'd been telling me one lie after another, just as serious as if every word he spoke was as true as the morning sun. I can't imagine where he gets all those stories. He was telling me about a lake in British Columbia where there are so many trout they have to swim standing up. He said he caught one fish there that was so big its photograph weighed thirty pounds.

I laughed and told Marv he was a work of fiction all by himself. I told him that from then on I was going to write down every story he told me. He just shook his head and said he was sorry, but he planned to stop telling them.

"I've got to quit doing that kind of thing," he said. "Do you know, I've been telling some of these lies for so long it's got so I believe them myself. Why, just the other day, I got to thinking about that time up on Rattlesnake Hill when I shot the elk with the seven-foot antlers and before I realized what I was doing I went looking through the garage to see if I could find the horns. And that's not the worst part. What really scared me was the darn things were there."

Well, I went ahead and wrote that story down, too, and about a hundred more that Marv has told me since then. For more than two years now, I've been hunting up stories and writing them down. Last summer, I finally got to hear Salty Johnson up at Timberline Lodge.

Actually, I didn't meet Salty at Timberline itself. The lodge is on the Manitoba side of Newton Lake. I met Salty at one of the lodge's outcamps, at a place called Breezy River at the northern end of the lake, up in the Northwest Territories. Salty used to trap all through that area back in the days before there was a lodge or anything else up there.

They say that Salty went for a whole year one time without seeing or talking to another human being. He just trapped and fished and took care of himself. That was back in the fifties. Nowadays, he lives in a little cabin not far from the Breezy River outcamp. Most of the time, he's off on his own, but once in a while he visits the camp and tells a few of his tales, like the one he told me about catching a three-foot pike with an even bigger fish inside it.

Marv and I had gone up to Timberline twice before we finally met Salty. We had quite a crew of folks there that day. That's when we had the liars contest. It's how this whole thing came together. But then, I guess that's getting ahead of my story.

Under the Walnut Tree

I'm sitting at the kitchen table, writing these tales and reminiscences on an old Underwood typewriter that I bought second-hand in 1947. It's six o'clock in the morning. There's a window next to the table and I can see a pileated woodpecker on the big walnut tree at the edge of the yard. The land slopes away from the house as far as the tree, then becomes quite steep for fifty feet or so before it comes to a small creek that runs through the middle of our property.

We only have ten acres here, but we're surrounded by forest. Deer come right into the yard. There's a raccoon family that comes regularly, too, and we've listed more than a hundred different kinds of birds that have been at our feeders at one time or another over the years we've lived here. All in all, it's a good spot for anyone interested in nature and the outdoors.

I suppose that old walnut at the edge of the yard is worth several thousand dollars if I'd cut it down and sell it. But I'd no more cut down that tree than I'd cut off one of my arms. It's huge, seventy feet high and a good three and a half feet in diameter. I've sat under that darn tree every fall for just about as many years as I can remember.

I first started coming here when I was a kid. Our farm was two miles down the road, nearly twice that far if you follow the creek. It was always a beautiful spot here, like a park even before we built the house and thinned out the trees in the yard.

I used to come up here in the fall to hunt squirrels. I'd kick up a pile of leaves under the walnut and stretch out with my back against its trunk. After a few minutes, the forest would come to life again. The birds would sing. I'd be able to hear the water rippling over the rocks in the creek below. Sometimes a squirrel would come out, but unless I'd been told to bring home something for supper, I wouldn't even bother to shoot it. Hunting was mostly just an excuse to sit under the tree.

It was also under that walnut, sitting on this hill overlooking the creek, that I shot my first deer. A boy's first buck is probably as exciting as anything else he'll ever do in hunting. I don't know what the regulations are now, but back then you had to be fourteen before you could get a deer license. I was way more anxious waiting to turn fourteen so I could buy that license than I was two years later waiting to get my driver's permit.

My birthday is in September, so it was over a month after I turned fourteen until the deer season opened. On the first morning, I got up before dawn, walked up the road and through the woods, and I was sitting right here when the sun came up. About an hour later, a nice six-point buck came out of the trees down by the creek. I'll never forget the look of him standing there, or how sad and elated I felt at the same time after I shot him.

Marv grew up on the other side of town, but he used to come here when we were boys, too. We used to meet here on days we wanted to hunt or fish or tramp through the woods. I used to trap all along the creek between here and Mud Lake. Marv had his traps out around Stevenson's Pond, but sometimes in the winter, after we'd both walked our trap line, we'd meet here, build a fire to keep warm, and sit around talking for hours at a time.

We started doing that just by accident. We knew each other in school, of course, but we were never close friends until one day when we chanced upon each other out here. Marv had come up the creek from Stevenson's Pond. I'd just finished checking my traps and had decided to continue upstream to an old drainage ditch that used to run into the creek on the far side of the hill. That's when I saw Marv trudging through the snow on the other side of the creek.

He said he was out exploring new country, looking for new places to trap. I told him I had this stretch of water pretty well sewed up. I'd meant to go up the little drainage ditch, looking for better spots myself, so Marv crossed the creek on a fallen tree and came along with me. Water in the creek moved too fast to ever freeze over, but there was a layer of ice on the ditch. We walked along on it watching the bank for muskrat holes and mink dens.

We'd only gone about a hundred feet or so when the ice gave way under Marv. It just opened a hole and he fell into it. It was like somebody opened a trap door under his feet. We were walking along talking and, suddenly, Marv was up to his armpits in water. I was standing two feet away from him, but the ice under me never even cracked.

I pulled Marv out and we came up on the hill here where we built a big fire so Marv could dry off. He stripped off the wettest of his clothes, including his pants and boots, and hung them over the fire while we sat and told stories. Even then, though, Marv told most of them.

In a half an hour or so everything was dry enough that he could get dressed and we resumed our walk. We kept well away from the spot Marv had gone through the ice, but twenty yards farther upstream the ice broke again. This time, though, it was me that went through and Marv who was left standing.

We rebuilt the fire and repeated the drying out process. The whole thing was so ridiculous we mostly just laughed at our own foolishness. But we've met out here regularly ever since. We've been meeting out here for fifty years now.

Of course, I built the house here thirty years ago so it's not quite the meeting place it used to be. On cold winter days we still warm ourselves in front of a fire, but now the fire's in a woodstove in my living room. Marv still tells as many stories as ever, though. In fact, when he got hooked up with Salty Johnson up at Breezy River he told more than ever. I guess it was the first time he'd ever come across anyone who knew as many stories as he did.

I first heard about Salty four or five years ago when Tom and Jean Benton came back from one of their trips to Timberline Lodge. They didn't meet Salty up there, but they learned all about him from the stories they heard. Tom told me some of those tales, but I'd have probably forgotten all about them if it hadn't been for an article about fishing that came out in the *Free Press* a couple of years ago.

Tom and Jean were just about to head back up to Newton Lake for their annual fishing trip when the article came out and Tom got so excited about it he carried the paper all over town for two days.

That's how I first saw the article. Tom gave me the paper, and of course, pointed out that Timberline was the place he and Jean disappeared to for a week every summer.

I didn't notice the article about Salty next to the one about Timberline until after Tom had left. As soon as I read about Salty, though, I knew I wanted to meet him. I had already started collecting these tales and I knew that anybody who'd spent his life hunting and fishing and trapping and living off the land like Salty would have good stories to tell.

The newspaper article said that Salty liked tall tales, which, of course, was just what I was looking for. They even had a couple of his yarns printed in the paper. My favorite was about hoop snakes.

Hoop snakes don't slither along on the ground the way most snakes do. Instead, they wind themselves into a hoop and roll along the countryside like a loose barrel ring, which is how they got their name.

They're also extremely poisonous. Marv told me once that when he was a young boy, back when his family was still farming with horses, a hoop snake killed one of his father's best plow horses. The snake didn't even bite the horse. It bit its collar and then wound itself up in a hoop and rolled away.

Marv's dad thought everything was safe then. After all, the snake had gone. But it turned out there was so much poison in that hoop snake bite that a few seconds later the horse collar started to swell up from all the venom. It swelled so fast that before Marv's dad could get it off, the darn thing choked the horse to death. That's the kind of poison you're dealing with in a hoop snake bite.

Marv says the only way to kill a hoop snake is to have two of them. What you do is stick the tail of the first snake into the mouth of the second and the tail of the second into the mouth of the first. That'll make them so mad that nine times out of ten they'll swallow each other.

In the newspaper article, Salty told about one time when he was walking around up on the tundra. I guess it must have been a nice day and he wasn't paying enough attention to where he was going because all at once he tripped over a nest of hoop snakes. Stepped right in the middle of them.

Salty said he jumped back out of that nest quicker than greased lightning on a summer Saturday night. Most of the snakes were so surprised at getting stepped on like that they rolled themselves into hoops and disappeared over the top of the next rise.

But the biggest snake of the bunch came out of that nest mad as a homeless hornet. He held his head in the air a foot and a half off the ground, hissing and spitting. Salty said the snake looked him right in the eye, took careful aim, and in an instant, struck with swift, deadly intent.

A little branch was all that saved Salty's life. He said that on parts of the Great Barrens, firewood is so scarce that he automatically picks up any scrap of wood he comes across. As luck would have it, that day, just before he stepped on the hoop snake nest, he'd noticed a small alder branch lying on the ground. Of course, he picked it up, intending to take it to the nearest cabin on his trap line to use for firewood the following winter. When the snake struck, Salty jumped back and swung that branch in front of him to protect himself.

The snake hit the branch with a smack, then fell to the ground. Apparently, the snake was injured because when it rolled away, Salty said, it rolled with a limp and looked flat on one side. Then Salty glanced down at his alder branch. That's when he realized what a close call he'd had with that snake. There, not even an inch below his hand, he could see the fang marks where that hoop snake had struck at him but had bit the alder branch by mistake. That's how close Salty had come to instant death.

Salty said there was so much poison in that snake bite, the wood began to swell from it as he stood looking at the alder branch. Wood was wood, though. Poisoned or not, he needed firewood, so he carted the branch off towards his cabin. He only got about a mile, though, because by that time the wood had swelled up to the size of a railroad tie and he couldn't carry it anymore.

He went back to his cabin for an axe, saw, and splitting wedge, but before he got back to the alder branch, it had swelled to the size of a telephone pole. Salty said he went right to work, but by the time he was able to cut everything up into fire logs, he had enough wood from that one alder branch to last him for three winters.

Even with all that extra firewood, though, Salty collected more whenever he found it. It's lucky he did, too, because if he hadn't, he'd have frozen to death the following winter. See, when the cold weather came, Salty tried to burn a couple of the logs from the alder branch the snake had bit, and it turned out the darn stuff wouldn't

catch fire. I guess there was so much snake poison in that wood all
it would do was lay there in the flames and hiss.

Reading that story was the only thing I needed to make me want
to meet and talk with Salty Johnson. I called Tom right away. He
told me how Salty had first come into the country around Newton
Lake back in the 1950s. Before that, he'd been a hunting guide in
Montana, then a trapper in Manitoba. For years, Salty trapped up
at Newton Lake all alone, only traveling back to the settlements
farther south once a year.

The lodge didn't get started until sometime in the 1980s. And
of course, even now, there are only people around during the summer.
Salty still spends every winter up at Newton Lake by himself,
although nowadays he stays in the lodge instead of up at his cabin
on Breezy River. There's a radio phone in case he needs to get in
touch with anyone and he looks after the lodge through the long,
dark days of winter.

At the time the newspaper story about Salty came out, Tom and
Jean were just getting ready to leave for Timberline. I called the lodge
to see if I could make a reservation, too, but I found out there wasn't
room for anyone else until August. In fact, except for a couple of
cancellations, there weren't any openings left until the following
summer. I was anxious to go, so I booked two spaces for the second
week in August and then drove over to Marv's to try to talk him
into going with me.

"I don't know," Marv said after I told him where I wanted to go
and how much it would cost. "I'm supposed to paint the house this
summer and I promised Betty we'd visit her brother in August. I don't
really have time for a fishing trip."

Then Marv smiled. "Maybe, if you'd twist my arm?" he said
holding it out where I could reach it. I grabbed his arm, but before
I could do anything else, Marv yelled for me to stop. "That's enough,"
he said. "I'll go. I'll go. Just don't hurt me like that."

The One
That Got Away

When it comes to telling stretched out yarns, stories about hunting and fishing must be where everything got started. The first fisherman who came home and told the story about the one that got away was the grandfather of all storytellers. You know what they say about fishermen? The only time they tell the truth is when they call other fishermen liars.

Mel Dixon used to run the coffee shop in Maple Valley and they say people accused him of telling so many fishing lies that he had to keep a set of scales in his restaurant. He'd bring in all the fish he caught just to prove they really did weigh as much as he said. Then one day Doc Stevenson borrowed the scales and the very next baby he delivered weighed thirty-seven pounds.

Until I met Salty up at Breezy River, Marv had always been the best storyteller I'd ever known. Of course, every hunter and fisherman that stumbles into Kelly's Tavern has a tall tale or two to tell, but it wasn't until the liars contest last summer that I'd ever heard anybody equal Marv for a steady stream of them. It's not that Marv's all talk. He's also the best woodsman I know. He just enjoys a funny story and he's never unhappy being the center of attention either.

One day last August, just after we got back from visiting Salty and the rest of the gang up at Breezy River, Marv stopped in here while I was working in the garden. We had good rains last summer and the whole garden looked really good. The tomato vines were six feet tall and the cucumbers, beans, peppers, and melons were thicker than I'd ever seen them.

11

I think it was probably the best garden we've ever grown, but it wasn't good enough for Marv. "Oh, this is nothing compared to the vegetables we grew at home a few years ago," he said. "Why, most of our tomatoes that year were the size of grapefruit and some of them were as big as pumpkins. The corn grew so fast the roots were drawn right up out of the ground like somebody had yanked on the stalks."

Marv also claimed to have had the best pepper crop he'd ever seen. "Why, those peppers turned as red as red-hot iron," he said. "At night, it looked like that whole corner of the garden was filled with little red lights. They were so hot the water sizzled when it rained on them. The whole family had to stay out of that part of the garden to keep from getting burned. We didn't have to weed because every time it rained the water would boil and scald all the weeds right out of the patch.

"My best crop that year was turnips. In fact, one of my turnips set a world record. I never sent in the particulars to the Guinness people, but there's no doubt my turnip was the biggest one ever grown. I think it all started because of the elephant manure I put in the garden that spring. I'd got it from old Charlie Frazer the year before, after the circus left town.

"At first, I just left that manure rot in a pile at the edge of the garden, but I mixed it around in the soil as thoroughly as possible once spring came. Then I gave everything a good tilling to work in all that composted elephant manure. I planted the turnips on the spot where the pile had been rotting all fall and winter and, afterwards, it seemed like this one plant just took off as soon as the seed was in the ground.

"I have to admit, I spoiled it a little. When I saw how fast it was growing, I watered it like crazy, five or six times a day, and I kept mixing more compost into the soil. I even ordered a dozen of those miracle fertilizer pills they advertise in the garden catalogues for growing giant pumpkins.

"When I gave the miracle pills to the turnip, it really started to put on weight. Why, by August, the darn thing had grown so much the top of it stuck out of the ground as high as my knee, and the leaves were over my head. It kept growing the rest of the summer and all that fall, too. Of course, by then, hunting season had started and I kind of forgot about it.

"That was the year they moved the start of deer season back to the end of November. Everything was kind of out of kilter for me then. I hunted pheasants and quail all through October, and in early November, when I should have been hunting deer, I mostly just took the dogs and went chasing rabbits.

"The funny thing was, the closer it got to the opening of deer season, the fewer signs of deer I saw in the woods. Deer get pretty wise as the hunting season approaches anyway, but this particular year they just seemed to disappear. As you know, I never have any trouble shooting my deer, but by opening day I was starting to worry. I mean, by that time, I hadn't seen a live deer in two or three weeks.

"I combed the woods all around home and never even came across a fresh track. I couldn't understand what happened to all those deer. It wasn't just me, all the neighbors said the same thing. We were all hiking farther and farther from home to look for that year's venison. It was as if the earth had just opened up and swallowed every deer in the area.

"By the end of the season, I was getting kind of depressed. After nearly fifty years of hunting deer, it looked like it would be my first time for getting skunked. On the last day of the season, I even thought about driving up north to see if I could shoot one there. But I'd always hiked into the woods right here at home to get my deer and I had no desire to change the way I did things. I didn't want to hunt anywhere I couldn't get to on foot.

"On the last day of the season, I got up early and sat on my back step. I was trying to figure out what to do, where to go. But I'd already checked every conceivable hiding place a deer could be. There just weren't any around.

"Finally, I got up and walked down to the garden, thinking I'd cut across to the back pasture and go over to Stevenson's Swamp. As I walked by the big turnip, though, I stopped dead in my tracks. A hunter has to keep his eyes and ears open at all times and I could hear the strangest sound as I stood there in the turnip patch. I couldn't figure out what it was at first. 'Crunch, crunch, crunch,' it went.

"I didn't know what to make of it so I walked around that big turnip until I found a big hole in its side where the noise seemed to be coming from. It sounded like a battalion of worms had got down that hole. I went to the garden shed for a hoe and when I came back I gave that turnip a good whack with the handle. When

I did that, a deer jumped out the hole and ran off. I gave the turnip another whack. Out came another deer.

"Well, when I saw that, I started beating on the turnip like I was a drummer in a rock and roll band and the deer just came pouring out the hole, a great big herd of them. They came through that hole like a bunch of sheep going through a pasture gate.

"It turned out that every deer in the area had been in the garden eating my turnip. They'd eaten so much of it they ate a hole right in the middle and then climbed inside where the turnip meat is tenderest. I hadn't noticed the hole because I'd been so busy in the woods hunting. But I got the biggest buck of my life that morning. All I had to do was wait until he came out of the turnip."

Of course, not all Marv's stories are as far-fetched as his turnip deer story. But sometimes, when you're hunting or fishing, the truth can be just as outrageous as a lie. Like the time Marv told me he had caught some sardines up at Rainbow Lake.

Everybody knows there aren't any sardines in any lake around here, but Marv stuck to his story. I asked him how many sardines he caught and he said a whole can full. It turns out that Marv snagged an unopened can of sardines while out fishing for pike one morning, so, in a way, he was telling the truth.

I think he was telling the truth, anyway. With Marv, you never know. He also told me once that he'd been fishing up at Marshall Lake when he snagged an old kerosene lantern and pulled it up on shore. "It had the date '1885' stamped on the bottom," Marv said. "So it was pretty old. But the really amazing part was that the lamp was still lit."

That's a lot like the story Salty told before the liars contest up at Breezy River. He said one spring out on the tundra, just at the time the caribou were coming through on their spring migration, he lost his pocket watch. It was a watch that had belonged to his grandfather so he hated to lose it. He spent a whole day going back over the trail where he'd lost it, searching in the lichen and rocks, but the watch was gone.

The next fall, though, Salty was out after winter meat during the autumn caribou run. He waited all day for the right animal to come along. Finally, towards evening, he saw one that looked familiar so he shot it. Sure enough, when he cleaned it, he found his watch inside. Salty said it was still running, too, and it was only about a minute and a half slow.

Another story of Marv's is about a time when he saw one of his cows catch a five-pound trout. Marv said the cow was crossing the creek when the trout bit on the knob of hair at the end of her tail. I guess it startled the cow so badly that by the time the fish let go, it was already half way to the barn.

Most of Marv's yarns might be hard to believe, but I'll tell you a true story that happened to me at about the same place on the creek Marv said the cow's trout came from. I was down there fishing when I snagged an old tire under the water at the edge of the creek.

I was just a kid then, fishing with an old cane pole, using that heavy black line everybody used back then. It was probably fifty-pound test. I backed up the bank and pulled the old tire out of the muck and up on shore. And I'll be darned if there weren't three catfish hiding inside the tire. That's the absolute truth, too.

Another story I believe is true, even though I wasn't there to see it happen, was the time Larry Munsinger was fishing on Slater's Creek over at Dover Crossing. I guess the wind came up and blew his fishing hat into the water. Larry's favorite lure was attached to his hat brim so he went running along the shore after it, but Larry's not much of a runner so the current took the hat downstream faster than he could keep up with it.

He was running along in his hip boots when he tripped over a log and fell in the mud. When he looked up, he saw a fish break the surface of the water and take the lure on his hat. Then the fish swam away with both his hat and lure.

I guess it was about a year later that Larry was sitting in the coffee shop when Marv came in. Marv right away told him that he'd caught a fish that morning that was wearing a hat. "And that hat must belong to you," Marv said. "Where else would a fish ever get one?"

And then there was that story Marv told about Larry a couple of years ago. It was in the fall, just like now. I think the story's true, but even if it isn't, it's still a fitting story about Larry.

According to Marv, Larry had decided to drive up to Pine Lake all by himself to go fishing. People say there's good fishing up there. I've heard all kinds of stories, but if you'd believe them all, there would have been more fish taken out of that lake than were ever in it.

I admit that it's pretty up there, but as far as I can tell, the lake's not worth the bother when it comes to fishing. On top of everything else, it's more than a hundred miles north of here. Why Larry would drive all that way by himself is more than I can understand.

He did, though, and he took along this old plywood rowboat his cousin Willie built a few years ago. I don't know what Larry did to make it leak, or maybe he didn't do anything, but he was over on the opposite shore from where all the cottages are when he first noticed the water in the boat. Larry said he figured he must have splashed some in with his oars so he just bailed it out and continued on with his fishing. In a few minutes, though, more water covered the floor of the boat.

That's when Larry should have guessed there was a leak, but he didn't. Instead, he bailed the boat again and continued on his way. The next time he looked at his feet, they were under water. He started bailing like crazy, but this time the water came in faster than he could get it out. About two minutes later, the boat sank and Larry lost a new Shimano rod and reel, a tackle box full of lures, a radio, a fishing vest that was supposed to float, and his shoes.

He was darn lucky he didn't drown, too, because Larry never was much of a swimmer and he hadn't brought a life jacket. He made it to shore, though, and built a big fire to dry his clothes. That's when the real fun started.

The weather was already getting chilly, late in the fall like that. Larry stripped down to nothing, draped his clothes over a couple of sticks propped over the fire, and tried to huddle close to the flames to stay warm.

He'd only been there a few minutes when he heard somebody coming. Being in a natural state of dress, Larry ran deeper into the woods so nobody would see him. When he looked back to see if anyone was coming, his clothes were on fire. He paused just for a second, wondering what to do next. Then he raced back to the fire and saved his hat. I don't know if his pants had already burned by that time or what, but he managed to get his hat.

He could still hear people coming along the shore, though, so he ran back to hide in the trees. Now what you have to remember is that Larry, to put it mildly, is rather rotund. He's so short and fat it's just about as easy to step over him as it is to walk around him. Marv says if Larry lies down on the ground and puts his hat on his belly, it looks like he's standing up.

Anyway, Larry's hiding there in the trees with nothing to wear except his hat and a grin when along came this group of hikers. Instead of owning up to his predicament, Larry stayed hidden until after they put out his fire and walked off. Then Larry snuck around the lake, through a little swamp, behind all the cottages, until he got back to the other side where he'd left his car. I guess it was a mile or two that he had to walk in his bare feet. His bare everything, for that matter.

If it hadn't been for the hide-a-key he kept under the hood of his car, he wouldn't have got home even then because he had forgotten his keys in his pants pocket back in the fire. Fortunately, Larry had left his wallet and lunch in the car, so he had money and something to eat. He thought about stopping somewhere to buy a new set of clothes, but he couldn't figure out how to make the purchase without drawing attention to himself. He decided, instead, to head for home just the way he was.

Larry's biggest fear was that the car would break down or he'd get a flat tire, but he made it back to Maple Valley without getting arrested. He only made one stop. It was for gas at a station on the highway outside Harrison. Larry put his hat in his lap, drove up to the pumps, and ordered ten dollars worth of super unleaded.

A young kid was pumping gas that day and Larry did his best to act as if there were nothing in the world unusual about a man driving around on a Saturday afternoon with no clothes on. Larry said the kid never said a word to him, although he caught the boy glancing at his hat a couple times while he washed the windshield.

You never know what's going to happen with Larry. I remember once he went on a hunting trip over in the Sherman Hills. It was about ten years ago and Larry had just bought a new Marlin rifle with a big Simmons scope on it. The first morning of the season, he was out early. Within an hour of sunup, he had bagged a big buck with only one shot.

I guess it was about the best shooting Larry had ever done and he was pretty excited about it. The first thing he wanted to do, of course, was take a snapshot of the deer. He laid his new rifle across the antlers and stepped back a few paces so he could get a better picture. When he looked through the camera lens, though, he saw the deer staggering to its feet.

Evidently, the animal had only been stunned when Larry shot

it. When he came to, it didn't take him long to run off, carrying Larry's new Marlin draped over his antlers. Larry didn't even have sense enough to take a picture as the deer ran away.

And he never did get his rifle back. Larry said he walked the woods over there every day for a month, but he never saw the deer or the Marlin again. That was a long time ago, maybe fifteen or twenty years, but Marv says he occasionally sees Larry's car parked along the road over in the hills. Marv claims Larry still goes out there to look for that rifle.

Cane Pole Fishing

When I was a kid, fishing meant an old cane pole equipped with a length of stout line, a bobber, a number ten hook, a couple of sinkers, and a worm. Sometimes, I'd use a night crawler for bait instead of a plain angle worm, and, once in a while, I'd get really fancy and use a cricket. Mostly, though, bait was something I dug in the garden.

I fished for bluegills and perch, and occasionally even caught smallmouth bass, off the dock at Mud Lake. I spent so much time down there in the summer I can remember lying in bed at night, my eyes closed, trying to go to sleep, but still seeing my bobber floating somewhere in my mind and memory. It would bob up and down a couple of times, then go under, then come back to the surface to bob about some more. It seemed like I watched that bobber all day, and then watched it all night, too.

Sometimes, I'd fish on the creek, usually off Carson's Bridge, hoping to entice a trout to take one of my worms. There were a lot of chubs and shiners in the creek that I'd have to throw back, but now and again I'd land a trout. I suppose I caught one just often enough to keep me going back after them. Once in a while, I'd run into a mess of rock bass. When that happened, fishing in the creek would be as good as in the lake.

I loved fishing then. Still do, of course. But back when all I had was a cane pole, that's when fishing was the best. As far as I was concerned, God had made the world two-thirds water and one-third land because he intended for us to spend one-third of our time

19

working and two-thirds of our time fishing. I'd experimented with my dad's bait-casting rod and reel, but a backlash had tangled the line so badly I stuck with my cane pole for a long time afterwards.

I was probably eleven or twelve before I learned to use a casting rod. About that same time, I bought a rod and reel and started fly fishing, too. It was quite a few years later that I began to hear stories about the new spinning gear that was just coming on the market. After that, nothing would do until I bought my own spinning outfit.

In the years since that first fly rod, I suppose I've bought a whole store full of fishing equipment. I almost never use anything but artificial lures now. I've got a big bass boat, an electronic fish finder, a couple of boxes of tackle, but fishing has never been any more fun than it was when I was a kid using a cane pole and garden worms.

Nobody needs expensive equipment to catch fish. A big bass isn't going to bite on a ten-dollar lure just because you did. The biggest fish I ever caught was the forty-pound lake trout I landed the summer before last up at Timberline Lodge. It was exciting. In fact, absolutely tremendous. But I can remember being just as excited with a three-pound bass I caught with a garden worm when I was a kid.

Talking about worms reminds me of something Marv said once when we were in school. Our science teacher, Miss Lewis, brought three night crawlers to class. She put one of them in a little saucer of whiskey, the second in a saucer of water, and the third in a saucer of Dr. Pepper. When she lifted the worms out of their saucers, two of them were soggy, but still crawling around. The one that had been in the whiskey, though, was dead.

After pointing this out, Miss Lewis asked Marv what he thought happened to people who drank whiskey. Marv squirmed for a second, then brightened. "I guess they don't have worms," he said.

Marv and I were best friends by that time. We lived to hunt and fish and be outdoors. Farm chores were just something we had to get out of the way so we could go to the woods. We pretty much ignored any school activities that weren't mandatory. No matter what came along, our standing response was that we had a pike fishing trip planned for that day so we wouldn't be able to participate. Sometimes, we'd change pike fishing to ice fishing if the weather demanded it, but we were never available for any kind of school stuff that wasn't required by law.

Over the years, between the two of us, Marv and I have used

just about all the different kinds of hunting and fishing equipment that have come on the market. When Marv's wife, Betty, gets after him for spending too much money on a fishing reel or new rifle or what have you, Marv always tells her that he got it on sale. "It only cost half what the ones that cost twice as much do," he says.

When I think about it, I've caught fish over the years on a real variety of gear. I even shot a nice bass once with a twenty-two rifle. Not many people can lay claim to that, especially the way I did it. I didn't break any fishing regulations or anything. It was back when I was about twenty years old and still going along with Marv on his coon hunts.

We were up on Smith's Ridge where the dogs had apparently treed three coons. At least we thought we saw three sets of eyes when we shined our light up the tree. The first two belonged to raccoons, but the third pair turned out to be something different. Marv was holding the light and I aimed for where I could see the reflection of an eye. When I shot, a huge smallmouth bass fell out of the tree. One of the coons must have taken it up there, but Marv said I'd shot a flying fish.

For years after that, I used to brag about shooting bass out of trees with a twenty-two. Then one day a couple of weeks ago, Marv told me that he shoots fish now, too. "In fact," he said, "I've decided it's the best way to get them. I don't shoot them out of trees, though. You spend too long waiting for them to come out of their holes if you do that.

"What I do is go down to the lake and pour a can of blue paint over the top of the water. Before long a fish will come swimming along and as he comes up to the surface of the water he picks up a coat of blue paint over his eyes so he just keeps on swimming higher and higher, thinking he's still in the water. That's when I shoot him out of the air. It's the best way to catch fish I know."

Despite what Marv says, and despite actually shooting a bass out of a tree once, I pretty well stick to traditional fishing methods these days. For the most part, I use a fly rod. I even tie a few of my own flies.

Once in a while, though, even today, I dig a can of worms and go down to Mud Lake. I've got an old row boat I keep down there and I take a twelve-foot, telescoping fiberglass pole I've owned for about twenty years. I usually go in the morning. The fog will just be coming in off the lake. I'll row out to a good spot I know for bluegills.

Then I'll just sit there and ponder world affairs while I watch my bobber. Sometimes, I ponder so much, I nearly fall asleep. It's not a bad way to spend a day. In fact, it's almost like being a kid fishing with a cane pole again.

Letting
Them Grow

After I talked Marv into coming with me on that first trip to Timberline Lodge, we still had more than a month to wait before we were supposed to leave. Most of that time we spent reading and re-reading the brochures the lodge sent us. We were only allowed to bring fifty pounds of gear, so we also spent a lot of time picking out clothes and equipment.

On the morning we left, Marv showed up with a new casting rod. I asked him where he'd gotten it and he claimed it belonged to his wife, Betty. "Wait a minute," I said, "Betty hates fishing almost as much as Lucille. Why would she ever buy an expensive rod like this one?"

"She didn't buy it," Marv said. "I gave it to her for her birthday last month."

Later that morning, we boarded a plane to Winnipeg. It was the first time Marv had ever flown and I could tell he was nervous. He had a pretty good grip on both arm rests during takeoff anyway, and he jumped, or at least looked up quickly, at any noise in the plane during the flight.

Once we got to Winnipeg, the lodge took care of everything. They had somebody waiting to meet us at the airport. We were taken to a hotel where they had a big banquet for all the fishermen coming in. All the food we wanted. The same thing at breakfast the next morning at six. Afterwards, they took us back to the airport for the flight up to the lodge.

Newton Lake was eight hundred miles farther north, so we still had a long airplane ride ahead of us. Fifteen minutes after we left Winnipeg, though, all we could see below were lakes and forests. We were leaving the world of cities and farms and small towns, traveling north to the subarctic, a place farther away from the lakes and rivers I fished back home than just the two thousand miles that showed on the map.

The plane, an old Hawker-Sidley, was full. A man and his son sat in the seats across the aisle. I could hear the father telling the boy about the lodge. "Good food," he said. "And lots of it." Other people sat quietly talking. Many of them appeared to have taken this same trip before. Marv leaned his head against the window and stared out at the trees and water below. I closed my eyes and tried to sleep.

A few hours later, a slight rumble came from under the plane as they lowered the landing gear. Marv sat up so fast he spilled the Pepsi he'd been drinking. The plane, flying much lower now, circled over a large lake and turned back south again, preparing to land. I could see several small buildings along the shore. "That's the lodge," I heard the man tell his son.

Marv stopped wiping the pop off his trousers long enough to get a good grip on the arm rests as the plane landed. As soon as it stopped, everyone got up at once. Everyone except Marv, anyway. He stayed in his seat, still occasionally wiping a paper napkin at his pants. I asked him how he liked the flight. "Oh, nothing to it," he said like a seasoned air traveler. "Just the same old thing. Up and down."

Marv and I were the last ones off the plane. At the top of the exit ramp, I stopped to look at where we were. The day was sunny and clear, the same as it had been in Winnipeg that morning. The runway was a long, rolling strip of sand and rock with stunted spruce trees growing on each side. There were no buildings in sight. I couldn't even see the lake. I followed Marv down the ramp. At the bottom, a man shook our hands and introduced himself. "I'm Garth Beddows," he said. "Welcome to Timberline Lodge."

Everyone else had shaken hands and continued on, but Marv stopped to talk so I did too. When we found out that Beddows owned the lodge, Marv asked about its catch and release policy. Except for smaller fish taken to eat for a shore lunch, Beddows said, every fish caught at Timberline was supposed to be returned to the water.

Of course, catch and release was fine with Marv and me. At one time, we used to keep every fish we caught over the legal length. Everybody used to do it that way. We judged the success of any fishing day by the number of fish we brought home for supper.

Then one day about thirty years ago, Marv and I were fishing up on the Big Mittibawassi River when he caught a huge pike. I don't know how big it really was because Marv never even measured it. But it looked to me to be close to four feet long. A real monster fish. After he landed it, Marv took out the hook and put the fish back in the water.

The pike looked pretty well worn out so Marv let it rest in his hands for a bit, gently moving it forward in the water to get the gills working. "Marv," I said, "what in the world do you think you're doing?"

Marv didn't answer. He just pushed that fish along through the water until, after a few seconds, it caught its breath and swam away on its own. In another moment, a few feet out in the river, the fish pushed a little rise in the current, then slapped its tail and was gone.

Marv continued watching in the direction the fish had gone. I couldn't believe what he'd done. "Marv," I said. "Why did you ever let a fish like that go."

"Oh, I don't know," he said as he turned back toward the river bank. "Nobody will believe me when I tell them I caught a fish that big anyway. I might just as well turn it loose."

Of course, that's not the real reason Marv let that fish go. He doesn't care if anybody believes his fishing stories or not. Just telling stories is what's important to him. He wanted to let the fish go so it would live and breed more fish that will grow to be as big.

Marv says it's just like raising cattle. If you keep taking the biggest animals out of your herd, it won't be long before you'll have a farm full of stunted cows. Everybody knows that. And it's the same thing if people take the biggest fish out of our lakes and rivers.

Marv claims it's always better fishing if you throw most of your fish back anyway. Keep a few smaller ones to eat, but that's all. Marv says that the way to catch big fish is to go alone and never bring your catch home. And especially don't get a trophy-sized fish mounted. "If you take a fish to a taxidermist," he says, "you'll stunt its growth."

On the other hand, according to Marv, if you've turned your fish loose, it will keep growing, getting bigger and bigger, so that five years down the line, the six-pound bass you caught will weigh at least ten pounds, and, of course, any story you tell about catching that fish will have to reflect its increased weight. Marv says that if you let your fish go, a lot of times it will gain three or four pounds before you can even get home to tell the story.

One of Marv's funniest tales is about a splake he caught through the ice up at the Collingwood Dam. Marv takes an old ice-shanty up there and leaves it every winter. I think he uses it as much to get away from all the other fishermen as he does to stay warm.

This one weekend, though, Marv said the fish hadn't been biting worth diddly. Nobody was catching anything. Marv said it didn't bother him any. He just locked himself in his shanty so he wouldn't have to listen to everybody else complain.

I guess Charlie Reid was doing most of the moaning about poor fishing. Charlie's that way anyway. He whines and complains about one thing or another most of the time. Marv says Charlie has such a big mouth that if it weren't for his ears, it'd look like the top of his head was an island.

Anyway, Marv said Charlie was fishing about thirty yards from his shanty. After a while, though, Charlie decided to go over on the other side of the river to see if anybody across there was getting any action. He left his fishing rig where it was and took off on his snowmobile, thinking he'd be right back.

A few minutes after Charlie left, Marv caught the first fish of the day, a nice-sized splake. The only thing was, the splake didn't really bite on Marv's bait. It had taken someone else's hook, then swam over and tangled itself in Marv's line. Marv just pulled it in.

He unhooked the fish, untangled the two lines, and then went out on the ice to see if he could figure out whose line he had snagged. That was easy enough to do since Charlie's was the only unattended line on that section of the ice. When he found out whose line he had, Marv went back and tied the end of it to the bench inside his shanty so Charlie wouldn't be able to get it back. He told everybody around what he'd done so they'd be in on the joke. Then he left the splake by the door to his shanty, and went back to fishing.

A little later, Charlie came roaring back on his snow machine. As he went by Marv's shanty, he saw the splake lying on the ice so he stopped to ask about it. "Nice fish," he told Marv.

"It's not bad," Marv said. "But I've caught a lot better ones."

"You haven't caught many better than this one," said Charlie. "In fact," he said, "if you don't want it, I'll give you five dollars for it right now. It doesn't look like I'll be catching any of my own today."

Marv agreed to the sale and Charlie took the fish back to his ice hole. Marv gave him time to get there, then he started pulling on Charlie's line. Charlie, of course, started yelling to everybody that he'd hooked a big fish. Marv let him take in some line now and again, but then he'd just pull it all back again.

By this time, Charlie was screaming that he'd hooked a sturgeon and everybody on the ice was laughing fit to be tied. After about ten minutes of this, Charlie finally got the idea that something must be going on, so he dropped his pole and started huffing all over the ice trying to figure out what everybody thought was so funny.

Finally, Marv stopped laughing long enough to come out of his shanty and tell Charlie what he'd been doing. Charlie got so mad he stormed off for home on his snowmobile. I guess he just left his gear on the ice. He was too angry to even stop and pick it up. What made him the maddest was paying five dollars for his own fish.

Marv just loves doing stuff like that, making somebody the butt of a joke. I remember one time in Kelly's when I was explaining an absolutely true story about a fish I'd hooked once, but lost, up at Kettle Creek. I had that fish right up at the boat before it got away, so I could see how big it was. When I told everybody about it, though, Marv just sat there with a big smirk on his face. I could tell he didn't believe anything I said.

"What's wrong, Marv?" I asked. "Don't you believe me?"

"Oh, I wouldn't say that," Marv said. "But I was just thinking how strange it is that none of the fish you let get away are little ones. Every fish I've ever heard you tell about getting away has always been a big one."

"Listen," I told him, "I'm not kidding about this one. I never saw a fish that big before in my life."

"Oh, I believe you," said Marv with a grin. "I believe you never saw a fish that big before in your life. In fact, you probably never saw a fish that big in your life, period."

Then I remembered a fish Marv had caught one time when we'd been fishing up north. "Well, one thing I know," I said. "My fish was definitely bigger than the one you caught up at Mede Lake."

Marv had caught that one in the lily pads. I guess his line was tangled in the weeds and he started screaming that he had a big one as soon as he began to reel it in. It turned out, though, that all he had, except for a few weeds, was this little bass about six inches long.

I teased him about catching such as big fish for several years after that. And that night in Kelly's, I told everybody that his fish was so small it took two men and a boy just to see it. I told the same story to Ralph and Eugene the first night we spent at Breezy River and Eugene told it to Salty the night we had the liars contest.

Denny Wayseecapo

After we got off the plane at Timberline that first summer, I stood and listened to Marv talk with Garth Beddows, but, at the same time, I was taking in the scenery around us. I'd expected land that far north to be flat, but from what we could see when we got off the plane, it was a gently rolling terrain not all that different from the way it is around home, except for the muskeg bogs that appeared to be at least as numerous as the hills.

The trees, though, were toothpicks not much taller than we were. The landing field itself had been built on a glacial esker so the land was sandy, with vegetation so sparse it reminded me of a desert.

Marv and I started down a trail behind the others, but as we walked we fell farther and farther behind. Every few steps, Marv stopped to look around. He stopped for every new bird. He stopped once to examine a rock. Sometimes, he just stopped to look at the stunted trees. He was the ultimate tourist.

After about a hundred yards, we came over a rise and saw Newton Lake for the first time since the plane landed. By the time we got down to the water, though, the boats that had been waiting there had already left for the lodge with everybody else.

A couple of empty sixteen-foot Lunds with twenty-horse Mercury outboards were tied to the dock. A Norseman float plane was at the end of the pier and a bearded man, dressed in bib overalls, was sitting on one of its wings dangling his feet over the water. "Another boat will be along pretty quick to take you up to the lodge," he said. "Or else you'll be able to get a ride up with Kenny or Garth. My name's Luck Winchester. I'm your friendly pilot."

I think Marv was afraid we were going to have to get into another airplane. "What do we need a pilot for?" he said. "We're already here."

"You're here, but those fellows up in the cabin there want to fly on to the outcamps. That's what we'll be doing as soon as Garth and Kenny get down here with their gear."

I turned and looked in the direction Luck Winchester had pointed. The cabin was on a knoll of land just above us. To the right, away from the landing field, was an open patch of sand and then more of the stunted spruce trees that covered the steeply rolling land around us. Obviously, despite the lodge's name, we were not yet above the timberline.

"How far north do you have to go before there aren't any trees?" I asked.

"Not very far," the pilot said. "Mostly, they're gone by the time you get a few miles beyond the lodge, except for along the shore. There are still trees three-quarters of the way up the lake if you stay close to the shore. There's even a few little spruce and tamarack along Breezy River. After that, though, you're pretty well on the Great Barrens."

From the end of the lake where the boats had disappeared, I heard another boat coming back across the water towards us. Marv and I watched as it came into sight. "That'll be your ride," said the pilot.

The boat continued at full speed until just before it reached the shore next to the dock. Then the driver cut the engine and the boat beached itself, perfectly, a few feet from us. "Been taking a nap this afternoon, Denny," said the pilot.

Denny just grinned. "Hop in," he said to Marv and me with an even bigger smile. "I'm your guide."

The trip down the lake to the lodge took about ten minutes, with the boat's fifteen-horsepower Merc going full tilt. As soon as we got to the lodge, we changed clothes, ate a quick meal, and headed back to the boat to go fishing. As it turned out, we couldn't have found a better guide than Denny Wayseecapo even if we'd ordered one special. He was just a kid, really, twenty-two years old, skinny, with a thin, patchy mustache. But he was good-humored, easy to get along with, worked hard, and knew where the fish were.

That first afternoon, we trolled off a large island a few miles from the lodge. We'd had a long day and, by the time we started, it was already mid-afternoon, so we didn't want to get too far away. We fished with Husky Devils on seventeen-pound-test line. Marv and I both caught several small lakers, so we felt like we'd been initiated by the time we were ready to head in to bed.

The funny thing about that first day was that most of the fish we caught were in the twelve- to fourteen-pound range, bigger than any lake trout Marv or I had ever caught. From what Denny told us about Newton Lake standards, though, they didn't amount to much, so we didn't get excited about them. Back home, we would have danced on the water if we'd caught lake trout that size, but even that first day at Newton we hardly batted an eye or said a word. On the way back to the lodge, though, I did notice a slight strain in my cheeks from grinning so much.

Denny said that the best fishing at Timberline was for lakers, but he assured us that the pike and grayling fishing were good there, too. He said the grayling stayed close to the shore around the inlets from creeks and rivers, as well as in the faster waters upstream. Pike were in the backwaters from one end of the lake to the other, but mostly they stayed at the south end.

Denny also told us we were unlikely to meet Salty Johnson at Timberline. Evidently, Salty stayed away from the lodge in the summer. He preferred to tell his stories to the smaller groups of fishermen who came to the outcamps. "And it's no use going up to his cabin to see him," Denny said. "In the first place, he's gone a lot in the summer, and even if he's there, if he doesn't feel like talking, he'll hide in the bush until you go away. Salty only talks when he wants to and then you can't shut him up."

Denny said that when Salty wanted to be with people, he usually went to the fishing camp up at Breezy River. Breezy River was only a few miles from his main cabin, and there were never more than a half a dozen fishermen there. When I heard that, I made up my mind to book a spot at Breezy River for the following summer. Breezy River was the farthest north of Timberline's four outcamps and, even if Salty didn't show up, I figured the fishing would be worth the trip.

The next morning, a Sunday, we were up early, on the water before six even though Denny said the best trout fishing started about ten. "They bite anytime up here, though," he said, so Marv and I figured we might as well be on the water early. We were only going to be at Timberline a week, so we wanted to get our money's worth while we had the chance.

The sky was clear again that first morning. Shirt sleeve weather on land, but even with only a light breeze it was five or ten degrees cooler on the water. This time, Denny took us farther north along the lake's west shore, traveling nearly an hour before he slowed the boat and we began to troll along the rocky dropoffs that plunged thirty feet or more from the shallow water along the shore.

Denny concentrated on the points of land that jutted out into the lake, but he always kept us traveling over the dropoffs. He constantly varied the engine speed. First slow. Then fast. Then somewhere in between. Then slow again.

He told us he came from a Chipewyan community a hundred and fifty miles south of Newton Lake. The village was a couple of hundred miles from the closest road to the south. As a boy, he sometimes skipped school in the winter and went with his father and five older brothers on their traplines.

The farthest he had ever been from home was Churchill, Manitoba, a town two hundred and fifty miles away on Hudson Bay. Churchill has a hospital and he went there to have his tonsils out when he was seven. He has never been back. Most of his brothers have been to Winnipeg, but Denny never has and he says he doesn't want to go.

Denny started guiding at Timberline when he was sixteen. "I didn't know anything then," he told us. "But they were short of guides up here so my brother Leonard got me the job. At home, we fish with nets so I didn't know anything about this kind of fishing. I didn't know the lake. I had to pretend that I knew where to go. My brother told me the spots to take people. Every night, he'd tell me where to go the next morning. Sometimes, I'd just follow his boat to the places he went."

We heard later that Denny had a lot more trouble when he started at Timberline than he told us. Garth Beddows, the owner, said that the very first customers he took out wanted to fish off Boundry Island on the other side of Birch Narrows.

Birch Narrows is only about fifty yards wide, and huge rocks are strewn all through it. Denny took Marv and I up there, so we saw what it's like. There are a lot of rocks hiding just below the surface of the water and, if you don't know where they are, it's not hard to hit one. Denny took it slow that first time through Birch Narrows, but he still had to dodge all over the place staying out of the way of those hidden rocks.

These guys he had with him were from Chicago and they began to get worried as the boat swerved in and out, bouncing back and forth between the rocks. They asked Denny how well he knew that part of the lake. Denny told them he knew every rock there. Just then, his boat crashed right into the top of a boulder. It made a great hollow bang and almost knocked his two clients out of the boat. Before they could say anything, though, Denny said "There's one of them now."

The very next day, with a dented boat and the same two fishermen, Denny went up into the Copper Islands, across the lake from where we were fishing that first morning. I guess when he got back in there among all those islands, it wasn't long before he got confused. His brother had told him about a good spot to fish in there, but he couldn't find the place.

After a couple of hours traveling around all those little islands he felt hopelessly lost. He took these two guys around and around, pretending that every place they came to he'd meant to bring them.

Finally, Denny started looking for an island where they could stop to have a shore lunch. All the nearby islands seemed too sheltered. Denny knew they'd be full of black flies and mosquitoes, so he kept his charges fishing for as long as he dared, taking them from place to place, all the while looking for somewhere to stop for lunch.

Eventually, though, he figured he had to stop and fix them something to eat. He headed for an island that looked like it had some high ground within reach of the shore. He figured if he could find a spot out in the open where the breeze kept the bugs to a tolerable level, they'd be all right.

Denny circled the island once, looking for a place where he could beach the boat and still be somewhere close to high ground. Finally, he pointed the boat towards a small rocky area on the shore. About twenty feet from the beach, he cut the motor and let the boat's momentum carry them in.

He moved to the front of the boat, and as it stopped in the water just short of the shore, Denny jumped for the nearest rock. I guess he only missed by a couple of inches, but the water was about ten feet deep there and he disappeared as fast as if he'd been a rock himself. He came up sputtering and coughing and the two guys from Chicago had to pull him back in the boat.

When you stop to think about it, it's no wonder Denny had a hard time getting started in the guiding business. He was only sixteen then, from an isolated community, probably not used to dealing with people. He had a lot to learn. Newton Lake is a hundred and fifty miles long. Some places it's more than forty miles across, and there are several hundred islands scattered from one end of the lake to the other.

Whatever problems he might have had guiding that first year, Denny definitely got over them. As far as I'm concerned, he's the best guide up there now, except for maybe his brother Leonard, who's the head guide at Timberline. Everybody says that Leonard's the best, even Denny.

But Denny is so easy to get along with, and he's got a wonderful sense of humor. One night at supper, Marv was bragging to everybody at our table about how many grayling he'd caught up on this little creek near the lodge.

None of it was true, of course. We'd fished most of the day on the lake and really did do well. But Marv didn't talk anything at all about that. See, we'd decided to quit early that day because it looked like a storm was coming. On the way back to the lodge, though, we saw where a small creek entered the lake and we decided to try it for grayling. Denny warned us that the black flies were bad, but we didn't listen.

As soon as we got in there, it started to rain, not much, just a little drizzle, but it really brought out the flies. They just ate us up. I never saw black flies so bad anywhere else at Newton and we saw some pretty bad places for black flies. Marv said that, at one point, they were so thick they lifted him right off the ground and he just sort of hovered there in the air for a second or two before they let him back down again. It wasn't that he was too heavy for them, he said, but they just figured they'd eat him right where he was.

On top of the black flies being so bad, the fishing was terrible. We didn't get one fish. Not even a strike. So we finally gave up and came in to supper: cold, wet, and just about ate up by black flies. I had a ring of bites around my waist two inches thick and Marv was even worse off. He had bites all over his belly and legs, even on his arms. Denny didn't say anything, but you could tell he was wondering why we bothered to hire a guide if we weren't going to listen to what he told us.

All the way back to the lodge, we talked about how bad the black flies had been. Marv said we shouldn't say anything about them to anybody else, though. He wanted to tell Frank and Tom, these two guys from Minneapolis that sat at our table, how incredibly good the fishing was up on that creek. True to form, Marv wanted Frank and Tom to go up there and get eaten by black flies just like we'd done.

And of course, Marv can't just tell a story and say the fishing was merely good. Once he got started telling his story, it automatically grew. The whole table stopped to listen, which only increased the size and number of the fish.

"They were biting on everything," Marv said. "The first half hour we were there, I caught thirty-five fish. They'd bite on red spinners as soon as the lures hit the water. In fact, sometimes a fish would jump out of the water and take a spinner before it even landed. This one big grayling jumped after one of mine while I was tying it on my line."

It was about this point in Marv's story when I noticed Denny. He had been walking by our table and had stopped to listen to Marv's tale. Marv noticed him at the same time, looked up and said, "Isn't that right, Denny?"

Denny just grinned. Then he said that something was sure biting out there because it had left marks all over Marv's arms. Of course, that drew everyone's attention to Marv's black fly bites.

"Yeah, that was the only bad thing about fishing that creek," Marv said. "There were a lot of hungry pike there, too, and they'd jump right out of the water after you if you got too close to shore. Mostly, I hid behind a tree, but when I'd cast out after a grayling, pike would jump up and snap at my arm. That's how I got all these little bites."

A Forty-Pound
Trout

We caught some big fish our first time up at Timberline. Lots of fifteen-pounders. Eleven that went over twenty. On the Thursday before we left, Marv caught a twenty-eight-pounder.

Of course, I wanted to catch a bigger one, but I didn't get anything to compare with it that day. At supper, Marv told everybody the fish had been biting so well, we had to hide our lures when we took them out of our tackle boxes. Otherwise, he said, the fish would jump right in the boat and take them away from us.

The next morning, Denny said he'd take us up to Slater Island. We'd been after him all week to take us farther north. The fishing wasn't necessarily any better there, but, since it was our first fishing trip up there, Marv and I wanted to get as far north as we possibly could. Or at least as far as sensible. We wanted to see as much of the lake as we could and still get in some fishing as we went.

Denny brought along an extra can of gasoline and we traveled for most of the morning. After a couple of hours, the spruce and tamarack trees began to grow farther apart, but the alder bushes seemed to grow thicker and more numerous. With its barren, rolling hills, the land looked more like parts of Montana or Wyoming than the flat tundra I had imagined before we came.

We didn't see much wildlife. Hawks mostly. A few Arctic terns, a parasitic jaeger. For awhile, a peregrine falcon followed the boat. We didn't see any mammals along the shore. We didn't see any other fishermen. The emptiest land I had ever known surrounded us. The lake went on and on. When we finally reached Slater Island, Denny said the mouth of Breezy River was still another four hours farther north.

At Slater Island, we began trolling. We had no more than got started when Marv pulled in a big one, a twenty-two-pounder. After that, we went around the island two more times without a strike. Then Denny cut across the channel to a point of land that jutted towards us from the mainland. I switched lures to try a chartreuse-colored Husky Junior, the one they call the potato bug.

Just after Denny swung the boat back south, hugging the dropoff close to the shore, Marv pulled up on his rod. "I'm snagged in the rocks," he said. Denny cut the engine. At the same instant, I felt a tug on my line. I started to say I'd caught a rock, too, but before I spoke I realized that what I had was alive.

I yanked up on my rod to set the hook and I knew right away whatever was at the other end was my biggest fish yet. There was a steady drag of line from the reel. I guess I had been trolling with about seventy-five feet of line out and I began trying to get some of it back. The fish, of course, had a different idea. He took the line slowly at first. Then the reel began to sing as he dove and ran. I made sure not to give the fish any slack, taking back as much line as I could whenever he circled.

After a couple of minutes, the big laker changed tactics. None of the lake trout we had caught fought with the frenzy of the smaller grayling, but, in some ways, this one seemed more like a sunken, motorized sack of potatoes than a fish. It fought, sure, but its tremendous weight was what made it different from other fish. Like most of the other trout I had caught, he tried to stay in the deep water. I brought him up slowly so the changing water pressure wouldn't rupture his air sack.

In every story I've ever read about catching a big fish, the writer knows to the minute how long the fight lasted. Somehow, I forgot to check my watch. I don't know if it took ten minutes or half an hour to get that fish to the boat, but, once it was close enough to see, I began to worry about my seventeen-pound-test line. I had no idea how much the fish weighed, but I knew it was a lot more than seventeen pounds.

Marv said the fish was too big for our net, so he leaned over the side and grabbed it with both hands to pull it into the boat. We didn't actually weigh it, of course, but Marv had a chart in his tackle box that told how to determine a laker's weight by measuring its length and girth. This one went just over forty pounds, more than fifteen pounds shy of the record for Newton Lake, but the biggest fish Marv or I had ever caught.

We got Denny to take our picture with it. The fish was so long I held its head and Marv held the tail. Then we lowered him back into the water and let him go. He swam along the boat, slowly at first, and then moved farther away into the deeper water. He seemed in good shape and I hope he lived. As funny as it sounds, watching him swim away was the highlight of the trip for me. Marv says he's going to wait a couple of years, so when we go back that fish will be big enough for *him* to catch.

After we let the fish go, Denny turned the boat north and we trolled along the same shore for a couple of miles, until we had just enough gas and time left in the day to get back home. I suppose we must have caught eight or ten more fish in the next forty-five minutes, but even though half of them went over twenty pounds, none of them was anywhere near as big as my forty-pounder.

Just before we turned back south towards the lodge, we saw another boat a mile or so away. Denny said it was probably somebody from the Breezy River camp who'd come south for the day. We waved, but the boat didn't come any closer, so we started towards it. The boat moved away from us. It looked like there was only one fisherman aboard. Denny stopped following it. It was time for us to head back to Timberline. He said the fisherman might be Salty Johnson anyway. "Salty could turn up anywhere on this lake," he said. "He has cabins all over up here."

The next morning was Saturday. We snuck off for an hour's fishing after breakfast, but then we had to get back and pack. It was time to go home. We flew in the same Hawker-Sidley going south, but, before we left, Marv and I made reservations for the following year. Only this time we booked a week in July at Breezy River. We both wanted more fishing like we'd just had, and I wanted to meet Salty Johnson.

When we got home I told everybody about my forty-pounder and Marv told everybody about a fish he'd caught that was so big he had to fashion the hook he caught it on out of a crowbar. "There weren't scales anywhere in Canada big enough to weigh him," Marv said, "and when we cut him open we found three caribou and an acre of tundra inside."

Somehow, even though I'd caught the biggest fish, Marv had outdone me again.

The Flight
to Breezy River

When we left Timberline that first summer, a year seemed like a long time to wait to come back. But as I get older, every year goes by faster than the previous one. Marv and I didn't do much fishing after we got home from Timberline, but it was almost fall by then, anyway, time for us to start getting ready for hunting.

What with pheasant season, duck season, deer season, bow season, and rabbit hunting, Marv and I keep pretty busy in the fall and winter. There's ice fishing, too, and, of course, Lucille and I have to go mushroom hunting every spring. Then, right after that, it's fishing season again. Before we knew it, Marv and I were on the Hawker-Sidley, heading north for Timberline Lodge.

This time, though, when we got there, we were the first ones off the airplane. Garth was there to greet us, just the way he'd been the first time. He told us to go down to the cabin by the dock, that coffee and snacks were waiting. He said Luck Winchester would begin flying people to the outcamps as soon as the gear was unloaded from the Hawker-Sidley.

Timberline has two other outcamps besides Breezy River, and, since they're all closer to the lodge, fishermen going to those camps are flown in first. There were six of us booked at Breezy, including two guys from Arkansas, Eugene Duncan and Ralph Thornapple. Eugene was a big fat guy, an electrical contractor who had a story of some kind to tell just about every time he opened his mouth. Ralph was a plumber who had fished at Breezy River several times before.

The other twosome was a husband and wife from Indianapolis,

41

Malcolm and Doris Chambers. He was a college professor. She was a real estate agent. As far as I could tell, Doris was the one interested in fishing. She was wearing a sweatshirt that said "Fishing: the art of casting, trolling, jigging, or spinning while freezing, sweating, swatting, or swearing."

We waited for nearly three hours for Luck to take the other passengers to their outcamps. Eugene must have thought there wasn't any food up at Breezy because, when our turn finally came to get on the float plane, he took about five pounds of cookies and a couple bottles of pop with him. "Got you a snack for the trip?" Ralph said as they climbed aboard.

Luck greeted Marv and me like we were old friends, Ralph too. "So you're going up to God's country this time, are you?" he said to Marv as he loaded our gear into the plane. When Luck got to Malcolm's stuff, he chewed the professor out for bringing more than the fifty pounds of equipment we were allowed. "This ain't no jumbo jet," Luck said. "If everybody did like that, I'd have to make an extra trip to Breezy just to haul baggage."

As the old Norseman lifted off the water, Luck told us that the plane had caught on fire a few days earlier. "Some fool smoking in the back caused it," he told us. This bit of news made Marv nervous again and, after a couple of minutes fidgeting, he asked Malcolm to put out his cigarette.

On the flight north, Luck took us out over the land on the east side of the lake, out beyond the tree line. When he finally circled back over the water, we could see three big snow drifts along the shore that hadn't melted yet. "Would you look at that," Eugene said. "Snow in July."

Malcolm asked Luck if we'd be sleeping in tents at the Breezy River camp and he looked relieved when Luck told him Breezy River had a bunkhouse with a woodstove for heat. Malcolm also asked if the cabin had electricity and Doris told us that her husband's idea of roughing it was watching black and white television.

A few minutes later, Luck pointed down to a small bay on the west side of the lake. He said it was the mouth of Breezy River. He took the plane in low over the water, following the river and stunted trees that lined both shores. Flying lower, the plane bounced and swayed more than it had at higher altitudes. Marv started fidgeting again.

Four miles upstream, Luck pointed at two buildings on a ridge above the river. The plane circled and I saw a man on the ground wave to us. "That's Denny down there," Luck said as he began his descent toward the water. "I forgot to tell you that he got a promotion. He's camp manager up here at Breezy now."

The Norseman touched down and roared along the water. "Whooeee," Eugene said letting out a big breath. I looked at Marv and guessed he felt the same way. After all the bouncing, I felt a little relieved myself.

After the plane slowed and started across the river toward the camp, Luck looked back at us. "Well, Marv," he said, "I guess we cheated death one more time." Marv grinned, but, for once, he didn't say anything. "Same old thing," I told Marv. "Up and down."

Luck maneuvered the plane up close to the dock, then cut the engine. Denny grabbed the side of the plane and pulled it closer. Luck jumped out and the two of them tied the plane to the pier. Then Luck pulled the side door open. "You folks might as well come out," he said. "You can't catch any fish in there."

Everybody climbed out and shook hands with Denny. "I haven't seen any of those man-eating pike since you left," he told Marv. Then he said for us to all go up to the cabin, that dinner was waiting. Luck said he had to get back to the lodge, but that he would return in a couple of days with a load of supplies for the camp.

Inside, Denny had a big meal waiting for us. Fried chicken. Mashed potatoes. Corn. Bannock. Lots of everything. After a day of traveling, we all dug in to the food. Eugene ate three or four helpings of everything. Once, when he asked Ralph to pass him the potatoes, Ralph told him to look out or he'd gain a bunch more weight.

Eugene just kept eating. "I never gain weight on fishin' trips," he said, pushing another fork full of mashed potatoes into his mouth. Ralph chuckled and told him that he had come out a few pounds ahead somewhere.

"This is nothin'," Eugene said. "You should see me eat when I'm at home. I remember this one time at a family reunion, I ate seven of them little chickens they sell at the grocery stores and a whole plate full of chicken salad sandwiches. When I got home, all I could do was sit in the corner and cackle. At first, my wife was going to send me to the doctor, but then she decided not to. She said she needed the extra eggs."

Malcolm chimed in to say that scientific experiments had proven you could eat twenty-five percent more calories in a day, and still not gain weight, if you spent at least ten hours outside. He said you didn't have to work or do anything special. You just had to be outside. Denny said that that must be why he stayed so skinny and Eugene said he'd be willing to eat a fir plank if somebody'd put peanut butter on it.

As soon as we finished eating, everybody wanted to go fishing. It was already past eight in the evening, but we were anxious to get on the water. Besides, in July, at that latitude, the sun stayed up until almost midnight anyway. Newton Lake and the biggest trout were four miles away, though, so we decided to stay close to camp and fish for grayling.

Ralph told us about a couple of sets of rapids a short distance away. He said there was also a small creek that fed into the river a little way past the rapids. All three spots, he said, were good grayling waters. We went in three boats. Eugene and Ralph stopped at the first set of rapids and fished from shore. Doris and Malcolm stopped at the second set and Marv and I went on upriver looking for the creek.

Ralph had told us it was less than a mile above the rapids, but it turned out to be at least twice that far. When we finally got there, we beached the boat on an island at the mouth of the creek and fished from there. It looked like the perfect place to catch grayling. We could fish the fast river water on both sides of the island, and we were close enough to the even faster creek waters to cast up in there, too.

We only caught a few grayling that night, though. Instead, we spent most of our time crouched under the boat. It had been sunny when we arrived at Breezy River, and there'd only been a few clouds when we came out after supper, so we didn't bring any rain gear.

Once we started fishing, though, storm clouds began to form and Marv and I started worrying about getting wet. "I do believe the weather can change in a hurry around here," Marv said, looking at the sky. In another ten seconds, the rain started.

We were too far away to go back to camp so we pulled the boat the rest of the way up on shore, emptied it, took the Merc off the back, and turned the boat over with one side leaning against a rock so we could crawl underneath. From there, we watched the wind whip past us, blowing the rain and loose spruce branches along with it.

Every black fly in the area apparently took refuge under our boat, too, and Marv and I took turns spraying each other with insect repellent. We sat where we were for more than an hour, trying to ignore the bugs, watching it rain, wishing we'd brought the rain gear we'd left back at camp.

When the rain began to let up, I looked out and saw the most beautiful rainbow I've ever seen. It was low in the eastern sky, arching over the river, and the colors were deep and true from one side of the horizon to the other. But the wind and rain were still too fierce to face without rain gear so we stayed put under the boat.

Finally, everything stopped. We figured we'd had enough fishing for one day so we put the boat back in the water and set off for camp. When we got there, everyone except Denny had already gone to bed. Denny said our four fishing companions had been scared off by the storm clouds and had returned to camp before the rain even started. "Well, for Pete's sake," said Marv, "whoever heard of a bunch of fishermen with sense enough to come in out of the rain."

Salty
Johnson

I woke up the next morning to the sounds of Denny and Eugene cooking pancakes. Before long, everybody was up, breakfast had been eaten, and Marv and I were packing our boat for our first full day of fishing.

By six o'clock, we were already trolling along the mouth of Breezy River. Ralph and Eugene had got out ahead of us, planning to go to an area Ralph knew on the other side of the lake. Doris and Malcolm were fishing farther south off a small chain of islands. There were no guides at the Breezy River camp, but we had good maps and Denny and Ralph had told us all about their favorite places to fish, so everybody had ideas about where to go.

Since Marv and I had brought our rain gear along, the day turned out to be almost perfect. Sunny and warm, with the fish biting intermittently all day. We didn't get anything exceptional that first morning, but each of us caught a couple of lakers right at the twenty-pound mark and a dozen others nearly as big. In the afternoon, we did almost as well. All and all, we figured it wasn't a bad haul for our first day.

That night, back at Breezy River, we found out everybody else had had the same good luck. Eugene and Ralph had mostly fished over on the east side of the lake and had caught a couple twenty-pounders and lots of others of respectable size. Doris had done about the same, but Malcolm, of all people, had caught a thirty-pounder off Abbott Island, a few miles south of Breezy Bay.

The next morning was sunny again and we headed for the open waters of Newton Lake even earlier. Denny had showed Marv and me a place called Wolf Narrows on our map. He said the fish had been biting like crazy up there for a couple of weeks. It was about thirty miles from the camp, but we fished most of the way up the lake, so we hadn't been there long when it started to rain.

A little rain, of course, wouldn't bother Marv and I. We had good rain gear this time and warm clothes underneath. Besides, the fishing was great. We'd caught fish all the way up the lake. Even after the rain started, we caught fish for an hour or so.

By noon, though, the wind had changed direction and was blowing hard out of the north, probably gusting up around twenty-five or thirty miles an hour. The temperature dropped about twenty degrees, too, and the fish disappeared to someplace where our Husky Devils couldn't find them.

After eating a soggy lunch in the cold, Marv and I began working our way back towards camp. We hadn't planned to pack it in, but we didn't want to go any farther away either. The wind got worse, so bad we had to stay as close to shore as we could, even though the fish were obviously somewhere else. The closer we got to Breezy River, the less we wanted to fish, but neither of us would dare be the first to suggest going in. Neither one of us were up to the kind of ridicule we'd get from the other one if we did that.

Marv piloted the boat along the west side of the lake while we both concentrated on staying warm and dry and pretended to fish. I was cold and tired. Marv slowed the boat down to a crawl. Then all at once he got a big grin on his face. "Say, you haven't seen it lightning, have you?" he asked, even though the rainy weather we were enduring was obviously no electrical storm.

I didn't catch on at first, though. "How about thunder then?" he suggested. When I said I hadn't heard any of that either, he asked if I were sure. Then a strained look suddenly came to his face and a flatulent rumble broke through the gentle purr of the slow-moving outboard.

"By golly, you're right," I said, finally catching on. "I think I did hear thunder. We'd better go in." Without another word, Marv and I began reeling in our lines.

"You can't be too careful with lightning," he said. "The reason lightning doesn't strike the same place twice is that the same place ain't there a second time." He opened up the throttle and we roared on back to camp.

When we got there, we were surprised to see Luck Winchester's Norseman tied to the dock. The Chambers' boat was parked beside Denny's and there was a third boat we didn't recognize. Ralph and Eugene were evidently still fishing. Marv and I gathered our gear and trudged up the hill to the cabin.

Inside, everyone was sitting at the big plank table in the middle of the room. Luck Winchester and Malcolm Chambers had their backs to us when we came in the door, but Luck turned around and grinned. "What's the matter?" he said. "You guys aren't letting a little rain and cold chase you in, are you?"

Doris and Denny were facing us, sitting on the opposite side of the table. A heavy-set man with about three days' worth of black and grey whiskers covering his face sat at the head of the table. Denny motioned for Marv and I to get a cup of coffee from the stove. When we did, he introduced us to Salty Johnson.

Salty, Denny told us, had arrived soon after we'd left that morning. He'd been on his way to one of his cabins on the other side of the lake. When the weather began to look threatening, he decided to stop at the camp until the storm passed.

Luck Winchester had arrived soon afterwards with a load of supplies. The storm hadn't started at the south end of the lake until after he'd left that morning, and it was just beginning in the north as he arrived, so Luck, too, had decided to stay at Breezy River until the weather cleared.

"Salty was just telling us about being snowed in once up here with another trapper named Sourdough Slim," Malcolm said.

"That's right," said Salty in a surprisingly high-pitched voice for such a big man. His eyes squinted across the table at us as he talked. "That was a time, I'll tell you," he said. "It was around back in the fifties, way before they constructed the lodge up here. The closest people were maybe two hundred miles south and we had three-day blizzards coming in here every two days.

"It was so frigidaire, whenever we went outside to get firewood, our tracks would run behind us trying to keep warm. One time, I went outside and my shadow froze to the snow so I had to chop it out with an ax before I could get back inside the cabin. The worst of it was we didn't have no grub.

"At the end of the second week, we had to eat Sourdough's dog in order to keep from starving to death. She was a nice dog, too. Her name was Sugar. As hungry as we were, she actually made a pretty good meal. In fact, she cooked up so good that afterwards Sourdough got to feeling sorry because he didn't have Sugar there to give the bones to.

"The blizzard kept blowing, so we couldn't get outside to hunt or trap any food. At the end of three weeks, there was nothing to eat but our shoe leather. We roasted it. We boiled it. We made soup out of it. Sourdough had a way to sauté it that wasn't bad. All I know is that our boots and a few pair of old moccasins and snowshoe strappings was what kept us alive until the weather finally broke.

"We ate shoe leather three times a day, every day, for six weeks. We ate it every way we could think to cook it. There must have been some food-nutrients in it, though, because at the end of that time I'd only lost three pounds, which I didn't much worry about because I'd been a little overweight on the fat side to begin with. The trouble is that, ever since that time, I haven't been able to stand the taste of shoe leather."

As Salty told his story, I slipped away to get one of the notebooks I'd brought with me from home. Now that I'd finally met Salty, I didn't want to forget any of his stories. I sat down again and started writing just as Salty finished his yarn about eating shoe leather. "Don't mind him," Marv said. "He's copying down tall tales. He wants to put them in a book."

"Well, I don't tell any tall tales," Salty said, taking a wad of snuff from a Copenhagen tin and tucking it into one of his cheeks. "Everything I've got to say is so accurate it's almost true. You might think it's a tall tale, but that's because this country up here is just so incredible-sighted to outsiders they always think my stories must be made up."

"I guess it gets pretty cold up here in the winter," Malcolm said.

"Oh, not too bad," said Salty. "A lot of days she'll warm up to about fifty below and sometimes the wind will drop down to no more than fifty or sixty miles an hour. That's the warm days. When it gets really frigidaire, that's when we have to look out.

"For one thing, up here you have to learn to walk with your head turned sideways. You don't dare face frontwards unless you stand absolutely still. That's because the weather's so cold your breath freezes as soon as it hits the air and if you're not breathing off to the side somewheres when you're walking, you'll run into your own breath and knock yourself silly.

"I can remember lots of nights when it's got so cold I've had to pull the woodstove into bed with me and nail the covers down just to stay warm. Even then, lots of times I'll have to get up during the night for more wood for the fire. One night, it was so cold the moon turned blue and all the planets huddled close together so they wouldn't freeze. I saw a shooting star freeze mid-fall and it never thawed enough to slip the rest of the way down to the horizon until the first day of summer.

"It was so windy one night that a big gust of cold air come through the keyhole and blew the legs off two chairs. It blew the socks off my feet and left my shoes where they were. Then that little gust of wind went to bouncing all over the cabin, blowing every which a way, tipping stuff over, rico-sashaying off the walls. All because it didn't have anywhere else to go.

"The window was shut up tight against the cold so that little wind couldn't get out until it finally happened to bounce off the far wall and go right back out the keyhole again. That darned wind had warmed up while it was in the cabin, though, so when it got back outside it melted a trail through the snow for a hundred yards before it finally disappeared into the trees."

"I don't see how you can stand it when it gets so cold," Malcolm said.

"Well, as tough as it is," Salty said, "I figure cold weather is better than hot. It's healthier for a person's health. It kind of instigates a man. Keeps a fellow active. Why, up here, we have to chop the ice off boiling coffee in order to pour it into a cup. That kind of thing builds character. Lots of times it's been so cold, I'll go out to shoot some meat—a moose or something that's maybe a mile or two away—and then afterwards I'll get back to the cabin before the sound of the gunshot.

"Sometimes, when you're out on the trail and there's no other way to keep from freezing, the only thing you can do to stay warm is sing 'In the Good Ol' Summertime' at the top of your voice. If it gets colder, you have to sing louder. And if it gets really cold, you have to sing songs like 'There's an Old Flame Burning Inside Me' or 'My Heart's on Fire.' Otherwise, your blood corporals will freeze.

"As I said, though, I'd sooner have the cold than the heat. I grew up on the Montana plains, so I know what heat's all about. Why, I've seen it so hot down there the corn popped right in the field and the thermometers all boiled dry. A lot of days it'd get so hot the tree stumps would crawl off to look for shade. One day, I was out fishing when somebody lit a match and the water caught fire. Another time, we hadn't even got to the lake when we met all the fish swimming up the road in the dust."

I asked Salty how, if he was born in Montana, he ever got way up into the Northwest Territories like he did. "Oh, there wasn't nothing specially unusual to it really," he said. "I grew up on a farm where the land was so poor it took ten quail to holler 'Bob White.' My mother used to fry pancakes so thin they only had one side.

"As soon as I was old enough, I struck out on my own and I guess my natural indigestion was to drift north whenever I wanted to go somewheres. Besides, there were too many people down there. It got so they was as thick as pig tracks around a corn crib and I decided it was time to leave. I had to find elbow room and I figured I might as well find room for the rest of me while I was at it.

"I run my own hunting lodge for a while up in the Bear Paw Mountains. Then, after that, I went trapping on my own. And every year, I kept going a little farther north. I stopped in a little town called Deer River once, but, for some reason, I just kept moving on.

"I always seemed to want to move farther north until finally I ended up here. When I saw how there weren't no graveyards, I figured it must be a pretty healthy spot. I come here to stay about 1957 and I haven't been any farther south than Thompson, Manitoba, since. In the old days, I lived pretty much off the land, too, hunting and fishing and living with what I could make myself."

"I guess you must have had trouble getting even the bare necessities into a place like this back before the lodge and all these people started coming around," Malcolm said.

Salty looked baffled for a moment. "The bare necessities?" he asked. Then he smiled. "Oh, it wasn't hard getting it," he said, "but about half the time it wasn't fit to drink."

Everybody laughed and then Marv suggested we purchase a case of the bare necessities from the camp store room. While Denny was getting the beer, Eugene and Ralph's boat came into view around the curve in the river below. "Well, this will make all of us," Marv said. "It don't look like anybody's going to do any more fishing today."

"No, the best fishing is always after a storm like this anyway," said Salty. "The weather's going to get worse before it gets better, but everything will clear off in the morning. That's the way it works up here."

"Yeah," said Luck. "That's the way it works except for the times when it doesn't clear off in the morning. There's been more than one time when I've been weathered in for two or three days during this kind of storm."

"Not storms like this one," said Salty. "We get storms that can last a week, even two weeks, three weeks, but when they come in like this, they're gone in twenty-four hours. You just watch and see."

"I guess you have special methods for predicting the weather up here?" Malcolm asked.

"The best way to fore-test the weather around here," Salty said, "is to keep a dog. If he comes in the cabin and he's all wet, it's probably raining."

"And if the lake freezes over," Luck added, "we're in for a cold spell."

In a few minutes, Ralph and Eugene came in carrying their gear. "Well, now I know why the fish quit biting," Ralph said. "You guys must have caught them all and quit early."

"That's not true," said Marv. "I left two fish out there for you guys, so you better go catch them while you've got the chance. You don't want to let a little rain and wind stop you."

"We'll just let 'em go," Eugene said. "I always leave one or two fish in a lake anyway. Besides, Ralph caught a twenty-five-pounder up at Thompson's Bay, and I caught a couple close to twenty, so it hasn't been a wasted effort. How about you, Malcolm? Did you catch another thirty-pounder today?" When Malcolm said that he hadn't, Eugene said, "Good. I'd have had to kill you if you'd caught another."

That's when Ralph noticed Salty sitting at the table. He said hello and introduced him to Eugene. Then he asked Salty how much the biggest fish he'd ever caught weighed.

"Oh, I can't rightly say," Salty said, "but this lake hasn't had any really big fish in it for years. When I first come up here, you wouldn't hardly catch anything under a hundred pounds. Lots of times, they'd go a thousand. Of course, the lake was a lot deeper then, and wider too. It was only after I fished all them big fish out of here that the lake shrunk down to the size it is now. A scientific fellow told me it was water misplacement that done it."

"If you've already fished all the big fish out of this lake, why have you stayed up here all these years?" asked Malcolm.

"Well, in the first place," Salty said. "I'm mostly up here for the trapping, but even that don't really matter because I just like living near Newton Lake. The way I figure it, this must be about the middle of the universe. All you got to do is just go out there on that hill when the weather clears up. Then, no matter what direction you look, why the horizons will be precisely the same distance away. And if that don't prove we're at the centre of the universe, I don't know what does."

"Where'd you get the name Salty?" I asked.

"Well, a lot of people think I got that name because I used to shoot with salted bullets," Salty said. "I had to do that because I was such a good shot I could hit a caribou several miles away. The problem was that after I'd shoot an animal at such a great distance, why by the time I'd hike out to get it the meat would already be starting to spoil from the wound. That's why I started salting bullets. That way, the salt preserved the meat until I could get there.

"That's not why people started calling me Salty, though. The real reason I got the name Salty is because when I first come into Manitoba, I needed a place to stay. I was trapping up along the north shore of Lake Winnipeg and I was so compounded busy, I didn't have time to make a proper cabin. I didn't even have any time to cut down trees for a cabin.

"One day, though, I come on a place where a bunch of beavers had cut down some trees. That give me an idea, so I salted the ends of each log and that night a bunch of porcupines came along and knawed on the salted areas just enough to put in notches. The next morning, I put the logs together and had myself a nice, snug log cabin, all because of the work of them porcupines and beavers. Folks started calling me Salty after that because of the genius-ability of my plan. The name's struck to me ever since."

Malcolm asked Salty what his real name was. Salty sat up straighter in his chair. He scowled and then leaned over and spit tobacco juice into a can under his chair. When he sat up again, he squinted even harder across the table at Malcolm. "Sidney," he said in his high-pitched voice, "and I'll whup anybody what calls me by that name."

Bells
and Bears

Nobody said anything for a minute or two after Salty told us his name. I could see Denny smiling. Doris picked up a copy of *Outdoor Life* off the window ledge behind her and started reading. Ralph went to his room and returned with a lightweight spinning reel and a small tool kit. He sat down at the table and began taking the reel apart. "I don't know why this thing had to wait until I'm up here before it decided to break," he said.

"It don't really matter," said Marv, nodding towards the window. "The weather out there looks like it's going to give you some time to fix it."

Eugene leaned back in his chair beside Ralph. "I never knew anybody named Salty before," he said, "but I did know an ol' boy one time they called 'Salt Lick.' He built himself a log cabin way up in the hills. Real pretty spot, too, 'bout fifty feet from the river, right on top of a natural salt lick. That's how he got his name. In the evenin', he'd sit out on his front porch watchin' deer and rabbits that'd come to his yard for the salt.

"Ol' Lick used to brag up his salt lick all the time. Tell about all the animals that came to it. Then, after he was there about six months, bears started comin' into the yard, and one evenin' he claimed he saw a panther. I don't know if he really did or not, but Lick thought he saw one and that was enough. It made him nervous about living where he did and he never talked much 'bout his natural salt lick after that. People just kept callin' him by that name."

I asked Salty if there were any bears or panthers around Newton

Lake and he said there were no panthers but plenty of bears. "I haven't reconspied a panther since I left Montana forty years ago," Salty said. "One time down there, I was scouting through country where both bears and mountain lions were troublesome thick.

"It was up on this little mountain in the Bear Paws. I guess I must have climbed about half way to the top when I come out on a ridge overlooking a small canyon. As I looked back behind me on the trail I'd just climbed, I saw a grizzly bear chasing after me. Then I glanced up in the tree beside me and spotted a mountain lion getting ready to jump on me. Just as the grizzly bear bounded the last few feet towards me, I lost my nerve for the fight and jumped over the cliff.

"As luckiness would have it, right then the grizzly bear made a grab for me. And at exactly the same instant, the mountain lion jumped to get me. But I went over the cliff, so the mountain lion ended up landing on the grizzly bear. Since the bear had been meaning to bite me in half, the mountain lion's head went right in the grizzly bear's open mouth. That made the grizzly bear mad and he bit the mountain lion's head off. The head got stuck in the grizzly bear's throat and choked him to death.

"In the meanwhiles, about ten foot over the cliff, my jacket caught on a tree branch, which saved me from falling into the canyon. After that, I just pulled myself back up to the trail where I skinned both animals." Salty slapped his knee and grinned. "And if you don't believe me," he said, "just come on home with me, because I've still got both the hides there to prove it."

Malcolm told Salty that he'd appreciated his story, but he was interested to learn what kind of bears were around Newton Lake. "Oh there's a whole parcel-post of them around here," Salty said. "Most of them are black bears, but there are a few Great Barrens grizzlies in the neighborhood, too."

"Are they dangerous?" Malcolm asked.

"Oh, not too dangerous," Salty said. "Just so long as they don't catch you. Actually, I fancy the grizzly bears around here. One saved my life once. I was lost in a frigidaire-blizzard and I happened to stumble into a bear den by mistake.

"I didn't know where I was until the blizzard ended. Then I discovered I was sleeping right next to a grizzly bear. He never woke up, but I figure it was heat from his body that kept my veins and articles from freezing shut and killing me. That's why I don't like shooting grizzly bears unless I have to. I wouldn't want to hurt an animal that saved my life."

"A grizzly bear almost ate me once," Marv said. "I had to climb a tree to get away from him and even then he would have got me except when I saw that he was getting ready to push the tree over I started sweating bullets. I guess it was a lucky shot, but one of them bullets hit him right between the eyes."

Doris put down her magazine and said that she'd heard a story one time about five grizzly bears who chased two hunters up a tree. They went right to the top of the tree, where the first hunter asked the second hunter to look down and see what the bears were doing.

The second hunter looked down and said, "Well, the good news is that all but one bear has given up and gone away. The bad news is that the one bear still here has a chain saw."

"Now that reminds me of another time when I had a narrow escapade from a grizzly bear," Salty said. "It was in the middle of winter, the weather was so cold the mercury wouldn't even come out of the thermometer bulb to sign up the temperature. I was just a young man then and accidentally by mistake I had disturbed a she-bear in her den.

"As soon as I saw she was awake, I took off running, but that bear chased after me for about a mile and a half. Then I come to a tree, so I climbed it. The old she-bear, though, she just knocked the tree over with one grrr-swipe of her paw. Before I could get to my feet, she grabbed right ahold of me and started shaking. It looked like I had to stay and fight or else get the glue-stickum shook right out of me.

"Well, I knew what I had to do, so I wrestled that bear for about fifteen or twenty minutes before I saw it wasn't going to be no use for winning. She was getting the better of me. She'd yanked the coat right off my back and I was about freezing to death, but it give me an idea. I grabbed my coat and covered the bear's head with it. I just wrapped the coat right over her head and held on tight.

"Now, I'll tell you, covering a bear's head is a good way to make her mad. Why, that bear went to hopping around there, growling and dancing. Of course, I couldn't really hear the growling because the weather was so frigidaire that day, but I could see what she was doing all right. Finally, I let go and the bear was so crazed she just run off and left me. I picked up my coat and went on home.

"The first thing I did when I got in the house was build up a big fire in the wood stove to try to get myself warm again after being out in that terrible coldness. I just threw my old coat down in a chair and built up the fire until it was about a hundred degrees above celsius-fahrenheit right there in the cabin.

"All of a sudden, though, I heard a bear growl. It about scared my socks off. Then I heard another growl, and another one. Pretty soon my old coat started jumping around there on the chair and a whole pile of growling and snorting noises started coming out of it.

"That's when I realized what was going on. See, it had been so cold out that all them bear growls had froze solid as soon as they hit the air. When I got that coat home, though, all them frozen growls and snorts inside it begin to thaw out and that's what caused all the racket."

"I'll tell you a true story about a bear," Eugene said.

"Now just a minute here," Salty interrupted. "Are you accusing me of telling a story that ain't true?"

"Oh no," said Eugene. "I'd never do nothin' like that. I just want everybody to know the story I'm a goin' to tell here really happened. See, I was over in Oklahoma at one of the state parks stayin' in a campground when this young bear come around and started terrorizin' all the campers. We yelled at it and the bear climbed a tree right in the middle of the campground.

"There was a young park ranger there who come over then and decided to shoot the bear with a tranquilizer bullet, so they could haul the bear somewhere else where there weren't so many people to bother. As it turned out, what happened next became a learnin' experience for the bear and the ranger.

"The ranger stood under the tree and shot the bear with the tranquilizer bullet. As a result, the bear learned not to come into the campground and to always watch out for men carryin' guns.

"Because the tranquilizer was also a muscle relaxant, as soon as the bear learned his lessons, he lost control of his intestinal tract and the ranger learned not to stand under a tree while shootin' a bear with a tranquilizer bullet. This lesson was reinforced a few seconds later when the bear fell on him. And that's an absolutely true story because I saw it happen myself."

"It reminds me of one time when I had a bear come right into my tent with me," Doris said. "About twenty years ago, I went backpacking up in the Rockies, up near Jasper, Alberta. I'd been out for about a week and was on my way back into Jasper when I stopped for the night at a place called Saturday Night Lake. It was less than a day's hike into town from there and I figured on being back before noon the next day. There were a couple other hikers at the camp there and we were sitting around my campfire drinking tea when we heard a bear in one of the other tents.

"We started yelling at it and the bear ran off, but he carried away a back pack that had been left in the tent. I guess the bear carried the pack about fifty yards or so, but when he dropped it, he ripped one of the pockets out of the pack and carried off a camera that had been inside it. We looked until sundown, but we never were able to find it. I told the fellow who owned it that it probably wasn't a bear that took his camera at all. It was probably a thief dressed up in a bear costume."

"I thought you said the bear came in your tent?" Marv asked.

"It did, or at least I assume it was the same bear. After we gave up looking for the camera we all said good night and went to bed. About four o'clock the next morning, just before the sun came up, I woke up hearing the wind blowing in the trees. At least, I thought it was the wind.

"I rolled over to get away from it and then I kind of woke up and thought, 'Gee, how come the wind left a wet spot on my ear.' I rolled back over and looked up at a bear bent over right there beside me in the tent. I guess he'd been sniffing in my ear.

"I'll tell you right now I let out a yell folks probably heard back in town. A half a second later, I was out the front door of the tent and the bear was out the hole he'd ripped in the back of the tent almost as fast. My scream evidently scared him as much as he scared me because we never saw anything more of him while we were there."

It seemed like everybody, except for Malcolm, had a bear story to tell. Eugene said that Doris shouldn't have got so upset at that bear, that all he was doing was giving her a kiss. He said a bear had done the same thing to him once.

Ralph told about a night in a fishing cabin in Arkansas when a bear had taken their catch and then stayed outside the cabin all night, keeping the campers inside hostages. "About three o'clock that morning," Ralph said, "I was still awake, sitting on my bunk. I hadn't heard anything outside for nearly an hour so I thought the bear had gone away. I got up and went to the window to look outside, and when I put my face to the glass to see into the dark, there was the bear with his face to the window looking back at me. It like to have scared me to death."

Denny told how his father used to trap bears in the spring and Luck told about a time he'd landed on a small northern lake and a bear had come up to where he'd beached the plane and chased him into the bush. Salty told another story about a time when he'd left early in the morning, before the sun had come up, to go to the other side of the lake. It was only after he'd gotten into his boat and pushed it away from shore, though, that he discovered a bear that had been sleeping in the stern.

Malcolm asked Salty what he did and Salty said that he decided right there that if he was going to the other side of the lake he would swim. He said he dove into the water and left the bear in the boat all by himself. He said the boat drifted out into the lake about a hundred yards before the bear jumped out and swam to shore. "I guess he didn't know how to run the motor," Salty said.

Malcolm didn't say anything for a second or two after that. I guess all the bear stories he'd been hearing worried him a little. "I've heard," he said to Salty, "that if you carry a bell tied to your pack while you're hiking through bear country, they won't disturb you."

"That's true," Salty said. "But it all depends on how fast you carry that bell."

Hoedads
and Hidebehinds

I suppose all the talk about bears made Malcolm a little uncomfortable. Salty's advice about carrying a bell didn't do anything to calm his fears either. When everyone stopped laughing, he asked Salty if the barren land grizzlies were the most dangerous animals in the area. "Or are the most dangerous animals wolves?" he asked.

"It ain't neither one of them," Salty said. "There are a lot of uncommonly dangerous animals up here, but wolves and bears are only mediocre-ish when it comes to dangerous. In fact, compared to arctic hidebehinds, I wouldn't call them dangerous at all."

"Arctic hidebehinds?" said Malcolm. "What in the world are arctic hidebehinds?"

"Oh, my whiskers, if they're not wicked," said Salty. "Why, an arctic hidebehind is the most feared animal of the North. They only come out at night so you rarely see them, but they lurk around all over the place when the sun goes down, especially on the darkest nights when the hiding is best.

"Hidebehinds are always hiding behind something. That's how they got their name. They can hide behind anything. Even objects that are only about half their own size. When you're out at night and a hidebehind comes along, you won't see him because he'll always be hiding behind something. You won't even know for sure that he's there at first, but after a while you'll get the feeling that something's following you. You'll just know that he's out there in the dark, stalking you, getting closer and closer until he's right-nearly behind you.

63

"Then you'll hear a noise and turn around to face the beast and he'll be gone. As fast as you can turn around, a hidebehind can hide behind something. You can never catch them sneaking up on you. About the only thing you can do to get away is to run for home. A hidebehind is fast, but, generally to speak of, not quite as fast as whoever they're chasing."

Salty slapped his knee, signaling it was time for everyone to laugh, but Eugene interrupted to say that he'd heard of hidebehinds and believed there was a southern species as well. He said that he, himself, had been followed through the woods several times by an Arkansas hidebehind and in Louisiana he had once come within a whisker of being captured by a swamp hidebehind.

All at once, Denny jumped up from the table. "Hidebehinds sound like strange animals," he said going into his room, "but I've got a strange one here that a guest gave me a couple weeks ago."

When Denny came out, he was carrying a stuffed animal of unusual design. At first, I thought it was a jackrabbit, but then I looked again and saw it had two straight horns coming out of the top of its head like a miniature antelope. "Does anybody know what this is?" Denny asked.

"Oh, come on, Denny," Marv said. "Any woodsman worth his salt knows a jackelope when he sees one. There used to be thousands of jackelopes all over the western half of the continent. There were more of them than buffalo at one time. The thing is, though, there's so much pollution nowadays there's only a few jackelope left."

"That's true," said Eugene. "This pollution is hurting a lot of the out-of-the-ordinary breeds of animals. The same thing has happened to bob-tailed lostandfounds. You almost never see 'em anymore, although there's still quite a few around."

Somebody had to ask what a bob-tailed lostandfound was so I figured it might as well be me.

"Well," Eugene said. "Of course, nobody has actually ever seen one, so we can only guess what they look like. They don't do no real harm, anyway. It's just that if you forget somethin' outside, they'll get it. The crazy critters will steal just about anything you forget in the woods. They especially go after kids' stuff, but they take anything. One got a huntin' jacket of mine just last fall."

Salty said he knew all about lostandfounds. "We've got 'em up here, too," he said. "Lots of them. Sometimes they'll even take things that ain't lost. You might think you know where something is, then all of a sudden it won't be there. When that happens, you can be as sure as shooting that a lostandfound has been around. Sometimes they'll come right in the house after things. One got a pair of my wool socks just the other day."

I asked Salty what other unusual animals they had in the Northwest Territories. "Oh my," he said. "There's a whole parcel-post of them. There are critters up here you just wouldn't believe unless you saw them for yourself. Take the long-tailed goofus bird, for instance."

"A long-tailed goofus bird," I said. "What's a long-tailed goofus bird?"

"Oh, there's lots of them up here," Salty said. "Anybody that's the least bit observatory can run across a couple dozen of them every day. The way you tell goofus birds is by their long tail feathers and the fact that they always fly backwards instead of forwards."

"Why do they always fly backwards?" I asked.

"Well, the way I understand it is that a goofus bird doesn't give a darn where it's going, it only wants to know where it's been. It even builds its nest upside down. In that regard, a goofus bird is a little like the deep-water heron.

"The deep-water heron?" I said. "Does it fly backwards, too."

"No," said Salty. "A deep-water heron don't fly backwards. It flies upside down."

"Why does it do that?"

"Well, I guess because it don't have no feathers on it's belly. See, a deep-water heron is about twice the size of a regular blue heron, and its beak is maybe three times as long. With its great long legs, and because it don't have belly feathers to worrisome about getting wet, deep-water herons can wade way out in the lake looking for food."

"But why does it fly upside down?" I asked again.

"Well, nature's ways are truly re-marvelous," Salty said. "If a deep-water heron flew right-side up, his belly would be in the shade of his body, and with no feathers on it, and all wet like that, he'd freeze to death in this cold climate. But if he flies upside down, why the sun is there to warm his undersides as he goes. It's the perfect adoption to a harsh climate."

"I don't suppose there are any other strange birds around here are there?"

"No," said Salty, "not unless you count the 'skeeters. Some of them are as big as eagles. I see them carry off small animals all the time. Two or three of them together can cart off a man. Or else one of them will try to hold you down while the other takes blood out of you.

"One time, I had a dog that got bit by a hoop snake. It was over about a mile from the cabin I've got right here on Breezy River. I didn't have no snake-bite kit, so there was no chance of saving the dog. I just tried to make the poor thing comfortable and left him setting there on the river bank to die in peace.

"The next morning, though, I come back with a shovel to bury the dog and here I see about two zillion dead 'skeeters laying all over the ground. Most of them were just normal-sized skeeters, but a few of them were hummingbird size and one or two were as big as eagles.

"Then the next thing I come to find out, there's my dog, running around barking, glad to see me. And him should have been dead. Then, of course, I figured out what happened. Those darn 'skeeters had come along there and went to biting the poor dog while he was laying there sick and they sucked all that poisoned blood right out of him. Got all the poison out and killed themselves with it, that's what happened."

Salty leaned over and spit in his can. Nobody said anything about mosquitoes or any other kind of strange animal for a minute or two after he finished his story about the dog. Denny went to get a few more logs for the fire. Then Malcolm asked if there were any other unusual creatures in the area. Salty said that most of the rest of them were standard varieties.

"What about hill-top plovers?" Marv asked. "They're pretty strange birds and I know they're around here because I saw one just this morning."

"Well now, that's true," said Salty. "I did forget about hill-top plovers."

"What are hill-top plovers?" Malcolm asked. "I didn't see one this morning, or any other time, for that matter."

Salty scratched his head. "A hill-top plover is a hard-falluting bird to describe," he said turning to Marv. "Maybe you could explain it to him?"

"Well," said Marv, "they're really not that much different than most any other plover, black and white with sort of tall legs. The thing that's different about them is that they only have one wing so they always fly in circles and spend their whole life flying around the top of one hill."

"That's right," said Salty. "I remember now. They nest on the ground like a regular plover, but in the winter, instead of flying south, they hibernate at the bottom of a sidehill dodger hole."

"A sidehill dodger?" Malcolm asked. "What's a sidehill dodger?"

"Now, I thought you were an outdoorsman," Salty said. "And you've never heard of a side-hill dodger?"

"No," Malcolm said. "There must not be any of them around home because I don't know anything about them."

"Well, if there were any there you'd see them all right," Salty said. "Anybody can see side-hill dodgers. They're not very big, about the size of a small coyote, but they're easy to spot anywhere there's hills. See, a side-hill dodger has legs on one side of its body that are longer than on the other side. That way it can run on the hills better.

"Of course, it can only run in one direction. If it goes in the other direction, with its short legs on the down-side of the hill, it will fall over and roll down the hill to the flat land where it can't do anything but walk in circles. Besides not wanting to fall off the hill, the other reason side-hill dodgers like to travel one-way roads is because their primary food course is hill-top plovers, and like I said, hill-top plovers only go one direction.

"Dodgers dig burrows all over the hills they live on and you can always see them running around, dodging in and out of burrows, chasing the plovers. They hibernate in winter, too, and as soon as they go to sleep, the plovers crawl in the same hole after them. Of course, the plovers don't have to worry about getting ate until the following spring when the flying and dodging starts all over again."

"Would you say that that's all the extraordinary animals you have up here, then?" Malcolm asked. "Now that you've told us about these plovers and dodgers."

"Well, so long as you don't count snow snakes," said Salty, "but they're only active in the winter and you never see them even then. They're too well camoflogged. See, the top half of a snow snake is white just like the snow so all you ever see are the wiggly trails they leave. In the summer, when the snow melts, the snakes turn over and go to sleep. Since their bellies are green like the grass, you never see them in summer either."

"What about beaver-pelted trout?" Ralph asked. "Not many people from down south know anything about them."

Malcolm asked what beaver-pelted trout were and Salty told him they were a huge trout variety that lived under glaciers and in the coldest parts of arctic lakes. They grow fur of approximately the same grade as prime beaver. "They're hard to trap," said Salty. "But the skins are naturally waterproof so you get good money for them."

"Speaking of fish," said Marv. "Are there any upland trout around here?"

"Upland trout?" Malcolm asked. "What are they?"

"Oh, they're one of the larger trouts we have at home," Marv said. "They build their nests in trees, but since they can fly they're difficult to catch. About the only bait they'll take are night crawlers and catalpa worms. We catch them with cane poles and number nine hooks, but they never go near water, so we have to use helium-filled balloons for bobbers."

"I guess you don't have any park hoedads around here do you, Salty?" Eugene asked. "We get a few of them farther south, but only in the national parks where they're protected from all the tourists. See, a park hoedad has front feet just like a bear's and back feet just like the hooves of a moose, so as you can imagine they're very hard to track.

"To complicate matters, when a hoedad gets tired of walking on four feet, he'll switch to two. Then, when he gets tired of walking on that pair he'll switch to the other pair. The tourists get so confused trying to track them they come home from the parks not knowing what they were chasing after."

"Oh, we've got the odd hoedad around here, too," said Salty, "but they're not the park variety. Park hoedads are just about as domesticated as old dairy cows. Up here, though, they're ornery as polar bears. Besides having front feet with claws like a bear and back feet like a moose, they've got teeth like a mountain lion, a horn in the middle of their forehead like a rhinoceros, ears like a rabbit, and a spiked tail like a tarantula.

"If that's not bad enough, they're faster than a cheetah, can jump higher than a kangaroo, swim better than an otter, change colors like a chameleon, lay more eggs than a chicken, and bark louder than a dog. The only reason there aren't more of them is that they have such a foul temper they can't even stand each other and the birth rate is extremely low. They're hard to hunt because on top of being fast, mean, hard to track, and nearly impossible to see, they rarely come out during the day so it's hard to get a good look at them."

"Did you ever try to hunt one?" Malcolm asked.

"Just once," said Salty. "I had a bad one getting after my trap line. He'd take anything I could catch before I'd get there to get it, so I had to do something. Otherwise, it's been my policy to avoid hoedads whenever possible. If they don't bother me, I don't want to bother them. But as I say, this one time I had to go on a hoedad hunt or just give up trapping.

"I guess it must have been about sundown on the third day when I come on him. I'd been tracking the varmit through a lot of thick brush and I was getting so scared my false teeth chattered even when I put them in my pocket. I'd just crossed through an alder thicket at the bottom of a creek bed.

"All at once, I could hear something moving. There was a loud splash in the water. I looked up and there was the biggest goldarned hoedad I'd ever seen. He was crossing the creek less than twenty-five feet away from me. He stopped for just a second and looked me right in the eye with the meanest, fiercest, most awfullest face I'd ever seen. I was too scared to think. I just closed my eyes and took two quick shots."

"Two quick shots," Malcolm said. "Did you get him?"

"Well, no," said Salty. "I told you hoedads were fast. By the time I took two quick shots and then got the cork back on the bottle, the blamed thing was gone."

Dry Creeks
and Talking Crows

Eugene laughed hardest at Salty's story about two quick shots, and then looked at Ralph, who had his reel scattered in pieces on the table in front of him. "I guess it must have been a hoedad what caused Ralph to take a couple shots too many that time up on the White River," he said.

Ralph turned away, shaking his head. "Oh, here we go again," he said.

"You should have seen ol' Ralph," said Eugene. "We were up there deer hunting a few years back and the last four days it like to have rained enough water for two or three lakes. It got so nobody even went outside. We just sat in the cabin playin' cards. Then, one night towards the end of the week, we decided we might as well go home as sit inside.

"By the time we come to that conclusion, though, ol' Ralph had already gone to bed. I think he'd been sippin' at a bottle of somethin' all day and he wasn't feelin' up to par. We got him up and put him in the car, but he fell asleep again as soon as we got movin'. There were four of us with all our gear piled in this old Ford station wagon.

"I don't s'pose we went ten miles before we come to a place where the river had rose up over the road. A real flood. But we looked her over pretty careful and decided we could make it across if we took her slow. I reckon it was maybe a hundred yards to the other side, but we couldn't tell for sure on account of the dark.

"Me and this other ol' boy climbed out on the hood to keep watch that we didn't drive into a hole or somethin' and the guy drivin' started

71

across goin' real careful. About half way over, the water got to slappin' up on the front grill so we stopped to survey the situation again. The driver clumb out on the hood and we all sat there tryin' to decide what to do.

"Meanwhile, inside the car, ol' Ralph woke up and figured we'd left him all by himself so he decided to come lookin' for us. We heard the car door open and then a kerplunk and a bunch of splashin' around. When we looked back, here was ol' Ralph face down on the middle of the river flappin' his arms about like a sick mud puppy."

"The worst of it was," Ralph said, "Old Eugene here wouldn't even stop laughin' long enough to help me out."

Salty said that story reminded him of a similar situation that had happened to him down in Montana. Only down there, it'd been just the opposite of too much water. "We'd gone trout fishing in a canoe up on the Manitou River," Salty said. "The fish weren't biting, so we just ended up paddling along sipping from a couple of bottles we'd brought for medicational purposes.

"The next morning, I woke up lying in the bottom of the canoe with a headache about like a war and my mouth as dry as a bale of cotton. I opened one eye and told my partner to give me some water. But he said he couldn't. Well that only made me mad. I wasn't asking him to fetch water from town, just to dip a cup over the side and get me a drink. I raised up and looked out of the canoe, and here we'd paddled about two miles up a dry creek."

"I suppose you must have had a hard time of it paddling the canoe back to the main river?" Marv said. "Or did you just leave the canoe and swim back?"

"Oh no," said Salty. "We didn't leave the canoe. We decided there must have been water in that creek at one time or another so we figured we'd wait it out. Sure enough, about two years later a flash flood come along and washed us right back out to the river." Salty slapped his knee.

"Do you know," said Marv, "I think what had to have happened there was that the creek must have rusted out. All that water probably just run out a hole someplace in the bottom."

Doris put down her *Outdoor Life*. "The first time Malcolm and I went fishing together," she said, "we went down to Morgan Lake in Indiana. They've got a big dam down there and there was great bass fishing in the undergrowth along the shores back then. We had a steel boat, though, which made for a lot of trouble going over sand bars and through all the shallow water where the biggest fish were.

"After a while, we got up in this little canal around a couple little islands and, sure enough, we run aground. Malcolm was sitting in the back and told me to take a paddle and push us away. Well, I took the paddle, but when I stuck it in the water it went down out of sight and still didn't touch bottom. I tried the other side. Nothing there.

"Malcolm kept hollering for me to push us away, that we were on a sand bar, and I kept telling him there was nothing to push away from. He got mad and came up to the front of the boat telling me he'd show me how to do it. Then he jabbed the oar over the side and come within about an inch of falling overboard. We were stuck, but the water was deep all the way around us. It was like we were anchored to something invisible.

"Finally, I took the oar and started poking around underneath and here we were sitting up on a big deadhead stump. I had to paddle the boat around and around until it finally slipped off the stump. I guess we must have been stuck there for a half an hour. Maybe more."

"You know what it is that got you off, don't you?" Marv said. "What you did by going around and around like that was screw that stump deeper under the water."

"I'll bet that's right," said Eugene. "Two bits says you were goin' clockwise, isn't that right now, Doris?"

"Reminds me of the time I was out here in the middle of Newton Lake," Salty said. "My paddle went and fell out of the canoe and floated away without my taking any notation of it. The day was calm, the water was almost like glass, but somehow or other my paddle just disappeared. I tried to get home paddling with my hands, but I realized right away it'd take about a week to get back that way."

"What'd you do?" Marv asked. "Swim?"

"Oh, no. I wouldn't swim," Salty said. "But back then the fish were so carnation thick all I had to do was wait for a big school of them to come along and then I walked across their backs all the way home. When I got there, I got me another paddle and walked back to the boat."

"Well, I'll be darn," Marv said. "I've often heard about lakes so full of fish the ducks walk on top of them, so I suppose what you say must be true."

"Of course, it's true," Salty replied. "Why back a few years ago here, when the fishing was still good, a person never had to worry about getting anything to eat up here. Even if you didn't like going out on the lake, you could still get all the fish you wanted. All you had to do was wait for night, because there were so darned many fish in the lake back then only about half of them could find a place to lie down. The rest all had to come up on shore to sleep.

"Of course, I've been other places where food hasn't been so plentiful as here. I remember one time on the farm down in Montana during a drought when we didn't have nothing to eat but gophers."

"Gophers?" Malcolm said. "How would you ever cook gopher meat?"

"Well, the best way to cook gopher meat," Salty said, "is to boil it for about three hours. Then bake it in an oven for another forty-five minutes. Then cut it up into small pieces and fry it in pig fat and onions for another hour. When it's finished, throw the whole mess away and cook you up some steak and beans like a civilized person."

"I heard of an ol' boy down home used to eat pole cat meat," Eugene said. "Said it toughened him up. Kept him from feelin' any pain."

"I suppose," Marv said, "that the last pain that man felt would have been when somebody cut off his nose so as he could eat pole cat."

"There used to be an old fellow up here named Beartrap Williams who was about the toughest fellow I ever knew," Salty said. "He used to pull his own teeth just for something to do. One time in a blizzard his ears froze off and he didn't even take notation they were gone until he went to scratch them. Another time, he cut off three fingers while he was whittling a stick and it was five days before he recollected they were missing.

"Beartrap claimed he'd only felt pain twice in his life. The first time happened one day when he'd stopped along a trail to take a crap and he accidentally sat on a beartrap. I imagine he would have felt a little hurt when that happened."

"When was the second time he felt pain?" Malcolm asked.

"Well, that," said Salty, "that would have been when he got to the end of the chain on that bear trap."

"Ralph," Luck said. "Did you tell these folks about that time a couple years ago when you and your buddies got lost over on Thompson Bay and had to spend the night out there? I guess that could have been a little painful, wouldn't you say?"

"Lost overnight?" Marv said to Ralph. "How did you stand the mosquitoes out there at night?"

"We just grabbed the littlest guy in the group, took off all his clothes, and tied him to a tree to divert them."

"How did you get lost?" Malcolm asked.

"It wasn't hard," Ralph said. "That was three years ago, my first trip up here. Everybody in camp decided to go over to Thompson Bay. The fishing was good, but when we stopped for a shore lunch, we decided to take a walk on some of the sand eskers close to shore there. This was at the end of August and it was about the first nice day we'd had all week.

"Unfortunately, after we'd walked around up there a while, we must have got turned around because when we went to hike back to the lake, we went the wrong way. By the time we realized we were lost, it was already getting along in the afternoon. We couldn't tell which way to go. Hell, everything looked so much alike even a compass would have gotten lost out there.

"We followed this one trail and it just kept getting smaller and smaller until it finally just ran up a tree. When the sun started to get low in the sky, about fifty million mosquitoes came out to get us. By then, we'd figured out which direction to go, but it took us a couple hours of walking and slapping bugs to get back to the lake. By the time we got there, it was already dark so we camped out on the shore until morning.

"The next day, we'd already started on the way back when we met Charlie, the camp manager, coming to get us. Most of us were just bug-bit and embarrassed, but one fellow from Chicago had a nervous breakdown and had to go home. He'd been all right while we were out there, but as soon as he saw Charlie coming after us he just kind of fell apart and started shivering."

"And, of course, the guy you tied to the tree was never heard from again," Marv said.

"That's right. He gave his life so that others might live. We only heard him scream once in the night and then everything was quiet."

"I guess one of them big 'skeeters just carried him off," Salty said.

"I've known 'skeeters to do that up here, although usually, at night like that, they'll just eat folks right on the spot.

"I shot a couple of caribou one time; hauled one back to camp, then went for the other. When I got back with that one, a big 'skeeter had gone and ate my first caribou and was sitting on a rock cleaning his teeth with the camp ax. I shot him with my 30/30, but not before he threw the ax at me. Almost hit me, too.

"He was a tough bugger, but 'skeeters up here are usually smarter than that one. If you catch them when they're a baby, you can even teach them tricks. I know a few fellows who have trained 'skeeters to keep the black flies away. They say if you work with them, you can even train them to talk, although I've never heard any talking 'skeeters myself."

"I know a guy trained a pet crow to talk once," Eugene said. "After a while, though, the crow escaped and went back to the wild. And before he knew it, all the crows for miles around was talkin' like college graduates."

"You were lucky that fellow that trained the first one wasn't a politician," Marv said. "If that crow would have learned to talk like a politician, you folks down there never would have got no rest."

"Oh, we wouldn't let politicians bother us," Eugene said. "We just live in a quiet little town. About the only thing around to do for excitement is have sleeping contests, ain't that right, Ralph?"

"I can't say as I know what you do for entertainment, Eugene."

"Speaking of politicians," Marv said, "do you know how to keep a politician from drowning?"

"No, I can't say as I do," said Eugene.

"Good," said Marv.

"Do you know the difference between a dead skunk and a dead politician in the middle of the road?" Luck asked. When nobody answered, he said it was the skid marks in front of the skunk.

"We don't mind politicians up here," said Salty. "It's usually so cold, they keep their hands in their *own* pockets."

"They might keep their hands in their own pockets," said Ralph, "but I doubt they do very much good either. None of the ones down home do much of anything when it comes to protecting the environment. They don't care about wildlife habitat or pollution, except at election time."

Doris started laughing. She was still reading the *Outdoor Life,* not listening to Ralph, but he didn't know that. "I guess I must be a real humorist," he said. "People laugh even when I'm not telling jokes."

"I wasn't laughing at you," Doris said, still chuckling. "I was just reading a story about an old poacher. His name is Rancid."

"I know an ol' boy down home that got arrested for poaching one time," Eugene said, "His name was Jim Talmadge and he didn't even do it. His dog did it."

"His dog did it?" said Marv. "How'd that happen?"

"Well, this dog was a wonderful dog as far as that goes," Eugene said. "He could retrieve anything. I guess that was the problem, too. See, this one year, just a day or two before pheasant season started, ol' Jim brought his dog with him squirrel huntin'. I s'pose the dog got bored sittin' under a tree and he wandered off. A little while later, Jim heard a shotgun go off, and a few minutes after that his dog comes back with a freshly shot pheasant in his mouth.

"That's when ol' Jim made his mistake. He put the pheasant in his pouch and went lookin' for the owner. A game warden found him first, though, and arrested him for huntin' pheasants out of season."

"Now, isn't that just like a game warden," said Marv. "Won't believe a man who says his dog committed the crime. Same thing happened to me one time when I was a kid. I was comin' home one morning, two weeks before the fishing season opened, with a big string of trout. And I'll be darned if the game warden didn't catch me.

"Do you know, try as I might, there was nothing I could say to that man to convince him that my dog had caught those trout. Not even when I showed him the place where old Bowser had carved his initials on the fish pole."

Guides and
Game Wardens

After Marv finished his story about getting caught trout fishing out of season, I asked him if he remembered the time Floyd and Harold Moseby got carried away and shot one too many pheasant over in the Sherman Hills. They'd already finished hunting and were on their way out of the field when they saw the game warden sitting in his truck parked on the road near where they'd left their car. Floyd slipped the extra bird out of his hunting pouch and tossed it out into the corn field so they wouldn't get caught with it.

When they got back to the car, the game warden came over and counted their birds. While he was counting, Floyd's dog, Lady, showed up with the pheasant Floyd had thrown away. I guess Floyd tried to hide it by standing between Lady and the game warden, but that just confused the dog and she walked around Floyd and laid the pheasant down in front of the warden.

He started laughing and told Floyd it was the first time he'd ever seen a hunting dog turn in his master on a wildlife violation. Floyd said the game warden laughed about it the whole time he was writing him up.

Luck said he heard of somebody once who left his dog in the car with a loaded rifle in the back window. A deer came along and the dog got all excited and went to barking and tearing around and the first thing you know he knocked the rifle down, the gun went off, and it shot the deer. "I say that'd be another example," Luck said, "of an out-of-season deer that'd be hard to explain to a game warden."

"There was an ol' boy down in Arkansas," Eugene said, "who had a bad reputation for poachin'. His name was Jeb Bumstead and he lived way back in the hills. All the game wardens knew about his misbehavin'. They tried all sorts of things, but they couldn't catch him at it.

"Finally, they got a new game warden who vowed he was going to nab ol' Jeb or know the reason why. This new fella went up in the hills like an undercover agent and, sure enough, not long afterwards, he run into Jeb out in the woods. The conservation officer wasn't wearin' no uniform and he was carryin' a gun like he was just out there huntin' too.

Jeb said hello and asked how the shootin' was goin'. 'Not too good,' the conservation officer said. He told Jeb he didn't believe there was any game left in the hills.

"Well, when Jeb heard that, he went to hee-haain' and slappin' his leg. 'No game left in the hills,' he said. 'Why I only been out huntin' a couple hours and I've already shot five 'possum and a buck deer.'

"Now, when the game warden heard about that deer, he figured he had ol' Jeb. 'Do you know you're talkin' to a game warden?' he asked. Ol' Jeb never flinched. 'No,' he said. 'But do you know you're a talkin' to the biggest liar in Arkansas?'"

I'd heard that same story told about somebody else in some other state, but I didn't say anything to Eugene. Ralph said that the game warden was lucky to get out of there with his life, that in the old days in the Ozarks, game wardens were thought of just about as highly as revenuers and water moccasins. "I can remember when I was a kid," he said, "there was a man in our town who people said had shot a game warden."

"I knew a fellow down in Great Falls," Salty said, "who was known to be the most orneriest poacher around. His name was Tobias. I can remember that, but I don't rightly remember if Tobias was his first name or his last name. But the game wardens was always after him.

"One day, he was up in the Sweetgrass Hills and he shot a nice big mule deer. Just after he finished cleaning it out, a game warden come along and asked to see his license. Well, this Tobias, he played around like he was looking for it, but he couldn't find it.

"The game warden, of course, didn't believe he had a hunting license to start with. Finally, he just says to Tobias that he was arresting him and taking the mule deer for evidence. I guess they were about three miles from a road, but old Tobias said he wouldn't help the game warden carry the animal. Said it would be against his Fifth Amendment right not to discriminate against himself. So the warden toted the deer down off the hill all alone.

"When they got down to the road, old Tobias got a big ol' grin on his face and said he'd just remembered where he'd left his license. He pulled off his boot and there it was. Ol' Tobias laughed about that one for years. He'd made that game warden carry his deer three miles to the road for him and then the poor fellow didn't even get to arrest him."

Luck spoke up next and said that there used to be a conservation officer back in his hometown in Manitoba who was known to turn a blind eye to an occasional hunting infraction. "When I was young," Luck said, "there were a lot of families like mine around who couldn't afford meat. If it hadn't been for home-grown hens and an occasional deer, legal or otherwise, we would have been involuntary vegetarians.

"I remember a story they told about this particular conservation officer. One summer, he'd stopped in to see a family in town who was known to eat fresh venison year round. Come to find out, they were just sitting down to dinner when the conservation officer arrived, and, being a hospitable family, they invited him to eat with them.

"Well, he agreed to that all right. He sat down at the table and proceeded to help himself to two or three helpings of everything, including fresh venison. He never asked any questions about where it came from, either. Then, when he got up to go, he thanked everybody for the dinner and told them it was about the best chicken he'd ever ate."

Doris asked if we'd heard the story about the guy out fishing with an expired license. A game warden came along and asked to see his fishing license and when the guy gave it to him, the game warden told him it wasn't any good. He said that the license had expired the year before.

"I know that," the guy fishing told the game warden. "But, you see, I'm only trying to catch some of the fish that got away from me last year."

"How about the fellow who was caught hunting deer after the season ended," said Luck. "When he went to court, the judge asked him why he didn't do his hunting during the season and the guy told him it was because it was too dangerous. He said there were too many other hunters in the woods during the season to hunt then. He got off, too. At least that's the way I heard the story."

"There's places down home where it really is too dangerous to hunt durin' the season," Eugene said. "I don't like bein' in the woods when the hunters are thicker than the deer. I've seen it where you have to get to a spot two hours before sunup so you can find a place to park your car. When it gets that crowded, I'd sooner take up somethin' else. Gettin' shot just plain spoils a huntin' trip for me."

"I live so far out in the country, we have to keep our own tomcat," Ralph said, "but it doesn't do any good come hunting season. There's so many deer hunters show up around there, I'm scared to take a walk on my own property. I have to go up to a place I know in the Ozarks to do my deer hunting."

"I wouldn't want to live where I couldn't go hunting right out my back door," Marv said. "It ruins it for me even having to get in a car to drive five miles. The only time I ever went deer hunting away from home, I went up north for a week with Stan Cummings and neither one of us shot a thing. When I got home, my wife had bagged a nice buck out behind the barn while I'd been away."

"You can be just as unsuccessful close to home as you can a long ways off," said Luck. "But the traveling expenses aren't so high."

"I knew a guy like Marv one time," Salty said. "He didn't like to leave home to do his hunting and fishing so he built his cabin out over the top of a stream. He fished off his front porch and never went no farther than the backyard for his venison."

Doris said that she'd once heard a story about a guy from New York City who went hunting up in the Adirondacks and shot what he thought was a deer. It was only about fifty yards away when he shot it but, before he could get to it, he saw a farmer go running over to the animal. The guy from New York figured the farmer was trying to steal his deer so he cocked his rifle and yelled at him to get away. He said the deer belonged to him.

"All right, all right," said the farmer. "Don't shoot. Just let me get my saddle and bridle off him first."

"You hear about people like that all the time," Doris said. "I've never seen it, but there's all kinds of stories about great white hunters who go deer hunting, or maybe moose hunting, and then come home with a dead cow tied to the hood of their car."

"Do you know," Salty said. "I used to run a hunting lodge up in the Bear Paw Mountains and, from my experiences, I'd say there's plenty of city people trying to be hunters that are just about that stupidified. Lots of them got vacant rooms to rent upstairs, I'd say. I remember these two lawyer fellows I took out bear hunting one time. I had a couple of stands about a mile apart baited with winter-killed cows and there'd been a monster bear in the area for about two weeks.

"I picked out the lawyer who looked like he had the most sense and left him by himself. I told him to get up in the blind, stay quiet, and not get too carried-away anxious when it came time to shoot. I didn't want him wounding my monster bear. I should have gone over the shooting instructions a little more, but I didn't realize I was dealing with a complete empty barrel. I just told him that if he aimed for a spot right behind the bear's shoulder, he could get a good, clean kill.

"Then I took the other lawyer fellow over to the second blind and we waited there in that stand together. I guess we were there three or four hours when, just at dusk, we heard something coming through the brush from the direction of the first blind. Then, all at once, he was there, the monster bear. He was a beautiful cinnamon boar, as big as a grizzly.

"I held up my hand and signaled my charge not to shoot until the bear got closer. The bear didn't stop at the bait. He darned near walked right under us instead, within ten or fifteen rods, anyway. But when my lawyer started shooting, he must have been aiming at angle worms. He shot three rounds into the dirt and the fourth into the side of a tree as the bear beat it for new territorials. It was plumb disgusting.

"We climbed down and went to see if this fellow's buddy had seen the bear too. When we got there, we found out he had. He said that the bear had ate at his bait for about fifteen minutes, but he hadn't been able to get a shot at it because the bear never turned his shoulder towards him.

"He said the bear stood up and looked right at him lots of times, but he was never able to draw a bead on the spot behind his shoulder. I asked the guy if he'd ever heard of shooting an animal between the eyes, but he evidently hadn't learned anything about that in lawyers' school.

"Another time," Salty said, "I took a couple guys from Los Angeles duck hunting and they turned out to be the terriblest shots I've ever seen. They were so bad, even the dogs got embarrassed for them and wandered off to hide. They wouldn't have anything to do with two fellows what couldn't hit the broad side of a barn from the inside.

"After we'd been out all day and they hadn't managed to shoot anything but time, this one lone duck flies over. I think the critter figured he wasn't going to make it all the way south anyway because he wasn't paying much attention to where he was going.

"He was flying low, so both these guys started shooting away like the Fourth of July. Of course, neither one of them hit the duck, but the bird circled back around and flew over us again. Both hunters opened up and shot until the muzzles on their guns were hot. They still didn't hit the duck, but I'll be darn if the bird didn't circle back and fly right over the blind again.

"The hunters opened fire one more time. Of course, they missed, but after that the duck just flew into a power line and admitted suicide that way. I tell you, it was dealing with people like those fellows that made me give up the guiding business. Why, some of them folks, I bet if you put one of their brains in a jay bird's head, he'd fly backwards.

Ducks, Bucks, Bears, and Beavers

All afternoon, the wind blew whitecaps across the river and hammered rain against the camp building's roof. Inside, we fed wood to the fire in the stove to keep the chill and dampness out of the air. We talked and told stories. Ralph gave up trying to fix his reel.

Now and again, someone would get up and stare out the window at the river and sky, wondering when we'd go fishing again. Sometime during the afternoon, Denny put a beef roast and couple dozen potatoes in the oven. By the time Salty finished his stories about guiding in Montana, it was time to eat supper.

Marv and I set the table. Eugene went outside for another armload of firewood. "We don't have weather like this in Arkansas," he said when he came back in. "It rains this hard. And it gets this cold ever' winter, but it never feels like this. It never feels so down right ornery. I've been in tornadoes when the weather felt more agreeable."

"One thing we don't look for much up here," Salty said, "is agreeable weather. We take the pretty days when they come, but we don't like to forget that the weather can turn troublesome on you anytime it takes the notion, winter or summer. Why, I remember one fall a few years back when the weather stayed just as sweet as the best day in July right through September. A lot of ducks and geese stuck around Breezy Bay way longer than when they normally head south.

"September thirtieth was absolutely beautatious, but when I went to bed that night I suspicioned a shift in the wind. Sure enough, sometime during the night, the weather turned cold enough for the lake to freeze over from one side to the other. It happened so fast all those ducks and geese that'd been at Breezy Bay waiting around to go south woke up in the morning froze in the ice.

"Well now, there wasn't nothing to do but harvest all those birds. I figured it'd be my winter supply of meat right there. There must have been a hundred of 'em. I walked out on the ice there, figuring I'd start with this old gander about fifty yards from shore.

"As I come up close to him, though, why he rared back and belted me with his wings, gave me a big old rap right side of the head. That's when I learned where the term 'goose bump' comes from. I picked myself up off the ice and tried to go at him from another direction, but he got me again.

"The dang bird made me so mad I decided to shoot him with my shotgun. When the shot went off, though, it scared every goose and duck on the ice and they rose up flapping their wings at the very same time trying to get away. Then I heard the ice cracking. It began way out in the lake, but then circled around all them ducks and geese and run up along the shore.

"Why, the first thing I knew, those birds were flying away, carrying about an acre of ice froze to their feet as they flew. Not to mention me, of course. As soon as I saw what was happening, I tried to make a run for it to shore, but by the time I got to the edge of the ice, we were already a hundred feet in the air.

"Well now, I didn't know what to do then. I knew, of course, they'd be heading south, so at first I figured the best thing to do would be to just ride along with them for a winter vacation. Then I got to thinking about that ice and I knew we wouldn't have to go very many miles south before the weather would warm up and the ice I was riding on would turn to rain.

"I didn't want to be a way up in the air when that happened. And since I didn't care to get any flying lessons where I was, and I'd plum forgot to bring my parachute, I figured I'd better change my mind about that vacation and start ciphering on some other way to get myself safely down on the ground. Then I got an idea. All I had to work with was my old Bowie knife, but I went at it, chipping ice and cutting those ducks and geese free one at a time.

"I'd only set fifty or so loose when I noticed the ice was starting to melt, so I went to working harder. And do you know, by the time we got down around Thompson, Manitoba, there were only a couple dozen big geese left and that ice had lost enough attitude that we weren't much higher than the tops of the trees.

"When I saw the Thompson airport coming into view, I started cutting the last of them geese free. I got it down to where it was just me and one big older gander and we come in for a landing all by ourselves. That's the last time I visited Thompson, too. I stayed there three weeks until the first snow and then bought a dog team and mushed my way home, three hundred miles. It took me about two weeks because all the rivers hadn't froze yet."

After Salty finished that story, we all sat down to supper and Marv asked him if he didn't get to keep any of those ducks and geese to eat. "No," Salty said. "I even missed that first one. He ducked his head just as I went to shoot. It reminds me of another time I went duck hunting and didn't get nothing but a moose for it. This was south of here a couple of hundred miles. I used to trap down there about thirty-five or forty years ago.

"But this persnickeder time, I got it in my head I wanted to have a duck dinner, so I went out and shot a few of them. On my way home, I was poking along through the bush watching for signs and places to trap when all at once I just about discombobulated myself tripping over a bear. It was getting way along in the fall and I figure that bear was just looking for a place to spend the winter when I came along and disturbed him.

"All I know for sure is that he was mad as a hungry trapper and he took off after me like I was breakfast. I lit out going for someplace I hadn't thought of yet and without stopping to cipher out what I was doing I scamper-scrambled up a tree. Of course, I was only up there about a second and half when I remembered that black bears didn't have no trouble climbing trees. I looked behind me and, sure enough, that bear was coming up after me.

"That's when I remembered those ducks. I pulled one out of my pouch and threw it down to the bear. Sure enough, he stopped climbing the tree and went back and ate the duck. When he finished, though, instead of going away, he came back and started shaking the tree until I threw him another bird.

"I rationed those ducks as best I could, but the dang bear kept coming back for more and I just didn't know how to say no. Just as soon as he'd eat one, he'd be back shaking that tree. If I didn't toss one down right away, he'd really go to shaking. I'd have to throw him another so as he wouldn't shake the whole tree down.

"Of course, my supply of ducks didn't last anywhere near as long as I wanted them to, and when he came back the last time I didn't know what I was going to do. That old bear went to shaking the tree so I was whipping back and forth up there like the end of a buggy whip in a trotting race.

"As luck would have it, though, just as the tree roots let go, I looked over and saw a moose running by. Well, I've always been quick on my feet. Lots of times I've jumped from one side of the river to the other and then back again without landing on the other side. So I made a leap and came down right on the moose.

"Of course, when I landed on his back, that old moose put on the steam. It wasn't hard for him to outrun the bear. In no time at all, we were away from the old bruin, but I had another troublesome problem on my hands. I was hanging on tight to the moose, but we were going too fast for me to get off. Besides, that moose was mad and I didn't want to be anywhere on the ground when we finally got rid of each other.

"My biggest problem was that I didn't know how to steer. I pulled on his horns and yelled gee and haa, but that old moose just kept going where he notioned. Then I figured out that if I reached up and covered one of his eyes, he'd kind or drift a little to the opposite direction. When I covered his right eye, he'd angle left. If I covered his left eye, he'd lean to the right.

"That's how I was able to gradually turn the cussed animal around and get him headed towards my cabin. At that time, I was trapping with a partner from Steep Rock, Manitoba, named Sam Stephenson, so as we started getting closer to home, I started yelling for Sam to open the door.

"Just as we come into the clearing in front of the cabin, I got that old moose aimed right and then I reached up and covered both his eyes at the same time. Of course, as fast as he was running he couldn't stop all at once. His momentum carried him across the clearing to the cabin, with me on his back yelling for Sam to open the door.

"Just two steps before we got to the cabin, I pulled my hands away and the moose looked up. When he saw he was going to crash into the side of the cabin he had a fatal heart attack right there. Just in the nick of time, Sam opened the door and we slid past him, landing in a pile on the other side of the room."

"I never knew anybody to ride a moose before," Eugene said when Salty finished his story, "but one time there was an ol' boy down home who rode a buck deer. He'd shot it, but I guess the deer was only stunned. Anyway, when he went to clean it out, he straddled the deer to get a good hold of it and the deer jumped up and run off with this ol' boy sittin' right up there on the shoulders.

"I guess he went darned near a hundred yards before he fell off. Later, he told his huntin' partner that the only reason he got off then was because he was afraid somebody would see that buck and start shootin' before noticing that somebody was a ridin' it. If it hadn't been so dangerous, he said, he'd have saddle-broke that buck and took him home."

"I never rode no deer or moose," Marv said, "but late one fall I had a bear chase me up a tree just the way that one did Salty. Except my tree was too small for the bear to climb. He went to shaking on it just the way Salty said his did, but the tree was well rooted and it held. Then the bear turned around and went away.

"I figured that he'd given up and it was safe to come down, but before I could do it, the bear came back carrying a beaver. I'd never seen anything like that before so I kept my eye on that old bear.

"Sure enough, he came right back over to the tree, sat the beaver down on the ground and the miserable rodent went to cutting down my tree. While he was working away there, though, the first snow of the year began to fall and before that beaver got half way through, the bear had to leave to hibernate for the winter, and once the bear went away, the beaver stopped working and left, too."

"Marv," Salty said. "I believe every word of that story is mostly true. I used to use beaver for cutting down trees myself back in the old days before we had chain saws. We could only get beavers to work in the middle of winter, though. You'd have to catch them a' bed to get them to do it.

"I'd dig an opening in the top of a beaver house, reach in and get a sleeping beaver while he was unconscientious. Then I'd take him out to where the trees were that I wanted to cut down. When I'd get there I'd just get me a good, long ice-cicle, ram it up the beaver's rear end, and when his teeth started chattering, I'd cut trees like I had a Husquavarna."

By the time Salty told that story, everybody but Eugene had finished eating, and Eugene was on his last round of potatoes. "That reminds me of an ol' boy down home," he said again. "His name was Amos Bontrigger. Orneriest ol' goat I ever come across, but one time he was out fishing and somehow or other he found this kit beaver. It was just a tiny little thing, hardly had its eyes open. I guess it got separated from its mother somehow, so ol' Amos took it home.

"When he got there, he had to figure out somethin' to feed this little thing. It so happened that his dog had just had a litter of pups, so he put the kit in with her. And do you know, they got along just fine. That ol' dog took to the kit beaver as if it were her own. Raised it up with the pups.

"The little beaver turned out to be a pretty good dog, too. It wasn't a good runner like the others, so it didn't go chasin' rabbits or anything like that, but it got to be an excellent watch beaver. Anybody come around the yard, boy, you can be sure they didn't mess with anything. Only a fool would take a chance gettin' bit by a critter with teeth like that. They called him Spike and I guess ol' Spike would still be alive today if he hadn't got started chasin' cars along the road there in front Amos's house."

"Why, what happened?" asked Malcolm. "Did Spike get hit by a car?"

"No." said Eugene, finishing his last bite of potato. "He didn't get hit by a car, but one of 'em slowed down enough that Spike snapped at its wheel. A lot of dogs that chase cars will do that. The trouble was, with that beaver's big teeth, why he punctured the tire and all that escapin' air blew him so far away nobody's seen him since."

Bird Dogs
and Dynamite

After supper, the conversation slowed down while the dishes were cleared. It was Ralph and Eugene's turn to clean up, but everybody helped. Ralph continued to tease Eugene about his appetite. "Do you know," he said, "we had a pie-eating contest once down home. Eugene won, of course. He ate about a hundred pies, but when he finished, he asked everybody not to tell his wife. He said if she found out she wouldn't give him any supper."

"Ralph," Eugene said, "sometimes I have trouble tellin' if you were born funny or just funny lookin'."

Gradually, most of us got sat back down at the table in the middle of the room. Doris kept saying she was going to go take a nap, but she never did. Salty was quiet for a while, but never moved from his spot at the head of the table. Marv got a can of Bear Grease and started polishing his boots.

"I never heard of a beaver acting like a watch dog," Salty finally said. I guess he'd been thinking about the story Eugene had told at dinner. "But thinking about it recollects for me about a mule we had when I was a boy. This old mule liked to go hunting so much he'd point sharp-tailed grouse and prairie chickens for us just so we'd take him along."

"I suppose he retrieved them for you too," Marv said. Salty claimed the mule did, although he said the animal had a hard mouth so they didn't like for him to do it.

"I had a dog with a hard mouth like that once," Marv said. "He was a good dog otherwise, but I could never break him of his bite,

91

so I finally just gave up on him as a bird dog and kept him as a pet. I named him Pal.

"Then one day, I was out fishing. Pal was along, of course. He went with me just about everyplace, so I took him fishing too. We were just sitting there in the boat when all at once I had a tremendous strike. I'd kind of dozed off at the time, so when the fish hit, he yanked the rod right out of my hands and pulled it into the lake. My old dog, Pal, didn't waste a second. He jumped in the water and retrieved my rod so I could land the fish."

"I hope you kept workin' with that dog," Eugene said, wiping his hands on the dish towel and coming over to sit down at the table again.

"A dog like that would have natural abilities," he said. "The same thing happened to me with a retrievin' dog once and I turned him into a first-rate trout hound. It got so anytime I'd hook into a big fish, I'd reel it back toward the boat, tire it out a bit, and then tell Corky—that was the dog's name—I'd tell Corky to go get the fish and he'd retrieve it for me. I never had to use a landin' net again after I once got Corky trained."

"I had a black labordog retriever that caught a fish once," Salty said. "That dog was the best duck hunter and retriever I've ever seen. It didn't matter where a duck would fall, old Duke would get it for me. This one time down on Delta Marsh, I shot a mallard out over the lake. Of course, Duke leaped in after it the instant the bird hit the water.

"When the dog got out there, though, I could tell something was wrong. He swam around, acting confused, like he didn't know which way to go. All at once, he dove under the water. A few seconds later, he come up about fifty feet away. Then he disappeared under the water again.

"He kept this up for about ten minutes, diving, then coming up someplace else. I thought the old fool had lost his senses out there, but he kept at it like he knew what he was doing. Finally, he made one last dive and when he came up he had a fish in his mouth, a big old jack fish, nearly as long as he was.

"I thought, what in carnation is going on here. It was a nice fish, don't you know, but that dog wasn't supposed to be bringing me fish. When he got back to shore, I took the pike and sent the dog back out after the duck. He'd never failed me before and I wasn't going to let him get away with it this time.

"Duke, though, just swam out a little way and then circled back towards shore. I'd yell at him to go back, to go get the duck, but he wouldn't do it. He wouldn't go no more than about ten feet out from shore before he'd circle around like he wanted to come back. I was sure mad, I'll tell you, and I made up my mind I wasn't going to let that dog come back without my duck.

"There was no point in wasting the pike, though, so while I was waiting for Duke to get some senses in his head, I cleaned the fish. That's when I ciphered out what had happened. See, the dog had been right all along. When I gutted the fish, I found my duck inside. That pike must have swallowed it before Duke could get to it, so that's why he went to chasing the fish. That's just how good a dog he was."

"Reminds me of a dog I heard of one time," Eugene said. "It was just a little mutt, but he was a son-of-a-gun for chasing sticks. Or anything else, for that matter. He was always hangin' around wantin' to fetch things for somebody. You could take a rock and throw it out in the water and he'd swim out and dive for it. He wouldn't necessarily bring back the same rock you threw, but he'd dive down and get you a rock, all right.

"This was down on the White River and the dog lived close to a bridge that used to be a pretty good fishin' hole. I guess this one day, a couple of fellows come along who weren't interested in fishin' like normal folks. They had some dynamite and they meant to get a bunch of fish the easy way. I don't even know if they noticed that little dog before they started.

"Anyway, this one fellow lit a half a stick of dynamite, threw it out in the water, and then watched as the dog dove in and retrieved it. Of course, when the dog come back with that dynamite these two fellows took off runnin' down the road. Trouble was, it was all just a game to the dog, so he chased after them, runnin' right at their heels until the explosion."

"I heard a story like that once," Marv said. "Only this happened to a couple of professional hunters out west. A bunch of sheep ranchers were having trouble with a wolf killing their livestock. It was a big wolf, with a missing toe on its right front foot. They'd tried for about six months to trap it, but hadn't been able to do it. Finally, they just gave up and hired these two professionals to do it for them.

"I guess these two fellows came in talking big, like they'd get rid of this old wolf in no time, but once they got started on it, they didn't have no more luck than the ranchers. They lived in this big hunting van equipped with all sorts of equipment. They had a bunch of rifles, traps, two-way radios. All kinds of stuff. And they had a couple good horses they towed around in a trailer hitched to the back of their van.

"But they trapped and hunted all over the countryside without even getting close to this blessed wolf. After a while, it became a matter of honor for them. I mean, they'd been trying to catch this one wolf for about six months, then a year, then two years. Everybody was laughing at them, but they made up their mind they wouldn't give up. They figured if they didn't catch that wolf before he died of old age, their reputation was shot.

"But everywhere they went, they were always a day or two behind this old lobo. Finally, they got lucky. The wolf had killed a single lamb at one ranch, and, knowing his pattern, the two hunters went to a nearby ranch and set a few coyote snares, something they hadn't been doing because they figured this wolf was too big and smart.

"The following morning, though, they had their wolf. Normally, they would have dispatched it in the quickest, most efficient way possible. But these two fellows hated this wolf so bad for causing them two years of shame and aggravation that they figured they'd get some revenge. They took a stick of dynamite from their van, tied it to the snare wire up near the wolf and then ran for cover.

"When they looked back, though, the wolf had broke loose from the log the snare had been tied to and he was running away, still attached to the snare and dynamite. To make matters just about as bad as they could get, as the wolf ran by their van, the dynamite slipped off the snare and blew up everything they owned except the horses they'd left to pasture a few miles away."

Salty wanted to know if the wolf got away and Marv said that it did. Then Salty said that hearing about a big wolf like that reminded him of a time when he was chased by an animal that was probably the biggest wolf on record, at least up until that time. "I'd been hunting up in the Duck Mountains," Salty said, "and I'd shot a couple good-sized elk. I was already on my way home with them, driving a horse and cutter, when I looked behind me, and here come a pack of a dozen wolves.

"Well, I whipped that horse, trying to get it to go faster, but the snow was deep and the wolves were gaining on us. I figured I better divert them, so I cut loose one of those elk and let it fall off for them to eat. A few minutes later, though, I looked back and here come the wolves again. They'd ate the elk and were after the other one.

"The horse still couldn't make any time, so I had to give up the second elk too. I figured I was done with them after that, but the wolves ate the second elk faster than the first one and then they started after me again. This time, I didn't have any elk meat to give them, so I turned and shot the big wolf at the front of the pack. And I'll be darned if the rest of the pack didn't stop to eat him.

"When they finished, though, they were off chasing me again, so I shot another one and the pack stopped to eat that one too. It happened over and over again. I'd shoot one, the pack would stop to eat, and then come after me again.

"Finally, there was just one wolf left. When he came after me, I shot him and skinned out the hide. And would you believe, that wolf pelt was the biggest one ever sold at the fur auction down in Winnipeg. Actually, I wasn't all that surprised at how big it was. After all, the darned thing had ate two elk and eleven other wolves just before I shot him."

After everyone groaned at Salty's story, Malcolm asked him to what he attributed his prowess as a marksman. "Well," Salty said, "a lot of it is natural disability, but I'd have to say the quality of the ammunition I use is important too. Years ago, you could get decent ammunition. Not like this stuff they sell today. I remember once back when I first started trapping. I was out in the woods all alone, sleeping in an old fall-down cabin, pitch black outside, when all at once I heard a terrible scream.

"Well, I want to tell you, I sat right up there in bed and listened. At first there was nothing, but then I heard a noise out in the trees. It was just a little noise, but it was there, all right, tramping around in the night. I knew I had to get up and find out what it was, but I was fidgety about it.

"I had to do something, though. I couldn't wait until whatever was out there come even closer, so I grabbed my rifle and clumb out of bed. There was a hole in the chinking on the same side of the cabin where the noises had been coming from, so I crept over there, stuck my gun out the hole, and fired.

"Well, let me tell you, I didn't get no more sleep from then on. All night long I kept hearing this buzzing sound going around and around the cabin. It about drove me to battiness. The next morning, though, just at sunup, I looked out and discovered that buzzing sound was only my bullet circling the cabin, waiting for daylight so it would be able to see good enough to hit whatever it was out there making all the racket."

Right after that, Marv told his old tale about not needing a gun or ammunition when he went hunting, that whenever he went into the woods the game just gave up and died when they saw him coming. I guess Marv thought he'd get the best of Salty with that story, but after Eugene chuckled at it a minute, he told Marv that he'd made a mistake. "It's not that those animals give up," he said. "The truth is, Marv, it's your ugly face that's killing them."

"My ugly face?" Marv said. "What kind of thing is that to say to somebody you hardly know?"

"I wouldn't say it, Marv, except I know a little bit about that sort of thing. It's a fact that some people are ugly enough to kill animals just by lookin' at 'em. I know a fella down home the same way. He does just like you do, goes huntin' without a gun. He uses his ugly face instead. His poor wife is twice as ugly as he is, but he saves her for big game."

When everybody stopped laughing at Marv, Ralph asked if we'd ever heard of Tennessee sheep. "They've got some honest to goodness sheep down there that are so skitterish, they'll fall down just like they're dead whenever they hear a loud noise. I know a guy was hunting one time when he came on a pasture of these sheep and a rabbit run out along the fence row. He pulled up his gun and fired and the whole flock fainted. He said he thought he'd killed them all."

"I guess that'd be quite a shot," Salty said. "I wish caribou would do that. It'd save a parcel-post of ammunition."

"I went frog hunting once," Marv said. "I was down in this old swamp full of frogs. All of a sudden, I saw one, so I shot at it and I'll be darn if five-hundred frogs didn't croak right then."

"The best shot I ever had," said Eugene, "was one time when I was duck huntin'. Two big mallards flew over, one above the other one, and I shot them both with one shot."

"Oh, I've had shots that good lots of times," said Marv. "One time, I was duck hunting when two ducks flew over and ran into each other, knocked themselves out, and fell right in the boat."

"Now wait a minute," Eugene said. "I'm not finished yet. I shot both of those ducks with one shot, but the first duck fell on a pheasant and killed it. The second duck fell on a rabbit and it done the same thing."

"Did you ever do any shooting like that, Salty?" Malcolm asked.

"Well, the closest I've ever come to marksmanslips like that," Salty said, "was down in the Interlake country in southern Manitoba. It was a real pretty day one fall and I'd been out deer hunting. I'd walked up on this little ridge over near Lake Winnipeg when I looked down and saw a big buck walking through the trees.

"I raised my gun to shoot, but just then I noticed a bear coming through the woods off to the left. I didn't know what to do at first, but then I got an idea. I took out my trusty bowie knife, threw it up in the air, raised my rifle and fired. Just as my bullet left the gun, the bowie knife come down and split it so as one half the bullet went to the left and hit the bear while the other half went to the right and killed the deer.

"Of course, the force of the bullet hitting my knife flung it forward through the air and it split a branch where six sharp-tailed grouse had perched. The branch sprung open, the knife passed through, and then the branch snapped shut again, capturing all but one of those six grouse.

"The most amazing part of the whole thing, though, was that when I went to clean the bear, I noticed he was all wet. Then I looked closer and saw a big old pickerel flopping around on the ground underneath him. I guess that old bear had just taken it out of the lake. So that meant that I'd killed a bear and a deer, captured five sharp-tailed grouse alive, and then caught a fresh pickerel to boot. I always figured that was fair to piddling for just one shot."

A Mad Coat
and Liars Contest

I don't suppose he meant to, but it was Ralph who got the idea of the liars contest going. "I don't know what anybody else thinks," he said after Salty finished his story about shooting the bear and deer with one shot, "but I'd say if we don't look out here one of these stories is going to get so stretched out it'll make somebody's ears swell shut."

"I wouldn't want to be responsible for anything happenin' to your health, Ralph," said Eugene. "But I don't think you've got too much to say when it comes to complainin' about tall stories. Why, Ralph, when I think of some of the lies you've got away with over the years, it makes me downright ashamed."

"What are you talking about, Eugene?" Ralph said. "I've never told you anything but the absolute truth."

"Yeah, and if anybody believes that, I've got some ocean front property in Arizona I'd like to sell 'em. I s'pose you're goin' to tell me that story about catchin' a coyote with your spinnin' rod is true."

"It is true," Ralph said. "It was up on Mullet Lake. I was bass fishing and made a bad cast into the lily pads. The tree frog I was using for bait landed on shore and when I went to reel him in, a coyote jumped out of the weeds and grabbed him. That's a true story."

"And you landed that coyote, did you?"

"Now, I never said I captured him. I said I caught him, and I did. For a while at least. Then he broke free and ran off."

Eugene shook his head. "I still think you tell so many stories that two or three times every week you have to get up in the middle of the night just to call yourself a liar."

"I never heard of anyone catching a coyote before," Doris said. "But Malcolm caught me once with a Wholla Popper. I was sitting in the boat minding my own business when he tried to make a cast and snagged me right behind my ear."

"Well, if you'd watch where you're sitting," Malcolm said. But before he could say more, Salty interrupted and told him he didn't want to hear any "marital discordents."

Then Marv said that he'd caught a coyote once. "I caught him by the tail," he said. "I did it with a bow and arrow. I shot him right through the tail and pinned him to an oak tree. Then I felt sorry for the poor thing and decided to let him go, but every time I went to pull the arrow out he'd jump and bite at me.

"I didn't know what to do then. I thought about it a minute, though, and got the idea of covering him up with something so he couldn't get me while I pulled the arrow out. I took my hunting vest off, threw it over the coyote's head, and buttoned it around him so he couldn't bite me. When I pulled the arrow out, the coyote popped his head out of the vest and ran off still wearing it. I never got that vest back either and I've been a little afraid to go in the woods ever since."

Malcolm asked Marv why he was afraid to go in the woods. "Oh, I guess I forgot to tell you," he said. "I had a half a dozen 30/30 cartridges in that vest. My guess is that as soon as the coyote gets his hands on a rifle, we're in for some serious trouble."

"He shouldn't have any trouble getting a gun," Luck said. "As long as he's wearing your vest, all he needs to do is go to a sporting goods store and buy one."

"Maybe he should get him a good huntin' cap while he's in there?" Eugene added. "And a pair of Eddie Bauer boots."

"I caught a coyote by the tail once," Salty said. "It was down in Montana. There had been stories about a rabid coyote going around for a couple weeks, but I never thought nothing about them. Then one day, on my way through a draw along a small creek, I stumbled across the critter that had been causing all the fuss.

"I didn't have a gun or anything at the time and this old coyote come right after me. Fortunate to goodness, I had a few yards head start on him and I made it to a big hollow cottonwood tree where

I crawled inside to hide. Before long, here come the coyote. I was afraid he was tracking me, but he wasn't. He was crazy mad and didn't know what he was doing. He came right up and sat down by the cottonwood. I could hear him panting on the other side, foaming at the mouth.

"Well, it just happened circumstantial that there was a knothole in that tree so I reached out and pulled the coyote's tail inside and tied it into a knot. That old coyote couldn't go anywhere after that. But I could, and you can bet more than last week's pay that I did, too."

Luck said that Salty's story about the rabid coyote reminded him about one time when there'd been a mad dog back in the town where he'd grown up. "It come walking right down Main Street," Luck said. "Nobody paid any attention to it at first, not until it was almost too late. There happened to be a bunch of us standing on the corner and all of a sudden the dog came at us barking and slobbering at the mouth.

"It was just fortunate the weather had been unusually mild that day. It was the middle of January and a buddy of mine had been wearing a big fur coat. With the sun out, he'd got so hot he took his coat off and was standing there holding it when the dog came after us.

"Not knowing what else to do, this fellow threw this fur coat over the dog and that's how everybody had enough time to get away without getting bit. Somebody ran and got a gun and we dispatched the dog before he could go after anybody else.

"The thing I wanted to tell you about, though, was this fellow's coat. I guess it was a week later I was sitting in a restaurant with him. It was cold enough that day to freeze a smokestack so he'd been wearing his fur coat again.

"Of course, he'd taken it off there in the restaurant. When we'd first come inside, he'd just thrown it over a chair there by our table. This fellow didn't know there was anything wrong with the coat at the time — except for a couple of tears where the dog had bit and clawed at it.

"All of a sudden, though, this old coat went to shaking and flopping around there on the chair until it fell off on the floor. Then it started in growling and barking. Finally, it let out a roar and stood up all by itself. That's when we saw it frothing at the collar. The cussed coat had caught the rabies from the dog. Of course, there was nothing to do for it except get it into a garment bag and send it to the dry cleaners to be put to sleep."

Doris said that Luck's tale about the fur coat reminded her of a story she'd heard one time about a woman who made a fur coat out of cat skins. The fur coat looked good enough, but everytime she walked by a dog, the coat hissed and its hair stood on end.

"Did that coat chase mice, too?" Salty asked.

"No," Doris said, "but it did its business in a kitty-litter box."

"I heard a story once about a cat with a wooden leg," Eugene said. "The cat walked with a limp, but it was still a good mouser. He'd just sneak up behind 'em and hit 'em over the head with his peg-leg."

"I think I'm starting to agree with Ralph," Malcolm said. "If lies were worth money, you folks would all be rich."

"Lies *are* worth money," Marv said. "They are if you're a lawyer or a politician, anyway."

"You guys can outlie any of them," Malcolm said.

And that's when Denny suggested we have a contest to see which one of us could tell the biggest yarn. Outside, the rain and wind showed no signs of letting up. No one would be doing any fishing that night.

"If you want us to have a liars contest, Denny, you'll have to start it," Luck said. Everyone agreed.

"Okay, then," Denny said. "I will tell you an old story I learned from my uncle."

And that's how the liars contest started:

"There was this guy up at Churchill on Hudson Bay," Denny began. "He could do everything better than anybody else. He could shoot straighter. He could run faster and farther. He could trap more animals and catch more fish. He was always bragging and after a while people got tired of it. No matter what they'd say, he'd say he did more, even if they were trying to give him credit for something.

"If he went out in the woods, they'd ask him if he shot a moose or a caribou. 'Two of each,' he'd say. If they asked him if he shot two moose, he'd say three. If they asked him if he ran ten miles, he'd say twenty.

"Anyway, this one day he said he was going swimming. Hudson Bay has ice over it almost all year long, but even in the middle of summer, after the ice goes, the water is still very cold. This guy didn't care, though. He wanted to go swimming. Everyone went down and watched him dive into the water and swim out of sight.

"He didn't come back all that day, or the next day, or the day after that. Finally, about two weeks later, they saw somebody swimming towards shore, moving across the water just like a speed boat. Sure enough, it was that guy. When he got back everybody asked him, where did he go? Miami Beach? He said that no, he didn't go to Miami Beach, but he stopped there on the way back."

I told the next story. I said that one time I'd been down at Mud Lake. It was a hot summer day, about the hottest day we'd ever had around home. It was too hot to fish and so dry you had to prime yourself to spit. It was too hot to do anything, so I was just sitting by the lake when I saw a fish jumping after a little frog.

The frog was hopping across the water like crazy, trying to get to shore. And every time that frog hopped, the fish jumped after him. But the fish would always miss because the weather was so hot. It was way over a hundred degrees that day and that fish just kept jumping after that frog and jumping after that frog until, I swear, that fish was wringing wet with sweat.

My story received polite chuckles and then Doris told a story about a hunter who became good friends with a deer. Two or three nights a week, this hunter and his deer friend would get together just as the sun was going down and talk and tell stories. One night, the hunter seemed particularly sad. "What's wrong, Tom," the deer said. "You can tell me, I'm your friend."

The hunter told the deer he'd been having money problems and the deer seemed sympathetic. After a while, though, she said she knew what Tom's problem was. She said he didn't know how to enjoy himself without spending a lot of money.

"When you have fun, Tom," she said, "you always go out to dinner, maybe go dancing, see a movie. The first thing you know, you spend twenty, thirty, maybe even forty or fifty dollars. But me, I can have lots of fun with just a couple of bucks."

Ralph told a story about a hunting dog he had owned a few years before. He said the dog was so good that one time, when it came to a point in front of a covey of quail, a rabbit ran past and the dog just reached out with one foot and stomped on the rabbit without breaking point. Another time, the dog flushed three pheasants. Ralph said he shot one. The dog caught another one, and the third one was so scared it flew into a tree and broke its neck.

Malcolm told the next story. He said that back in Indiana, it gets windy a lot. He said that one time it was so windy he saw a chicken lay the same egg three times. Another time he'd been out hunting when the wind started blowing. Just about then, his dogs scared up a rabbit and started chasing it. When the rabbit saw the dogs, though, he just raised his ears and the wind blew him away.

"That's not the story I meant to tell you, though," Malcolm said. "The story I meant to tell you was about the first time Doris and I ever went camping together. We went up to Wilderness State Park in northern Michigan. When we got there, we found out they'd been having problems with bears. They'd been making trouble in the campgrounds all that summer.

"Well, bears make me nervous. I don't really like to think about them, but it was Doris who kept me from sleeping that first night. See, as we were getting ready to turn in, I saw her put a pair of running shoes by the door of the tent and I asked her what she was doing that for.

"She told me she wanted to leave the shoes there so she could get them on in a hurry in case a bear came after us. Well, I thought that was pretty stupid, so I told her not to be ridiculous, that a bear could run faster than she could no matter what kind of shoes she wore.

"'That might be true,' she told me, 'but the way I figure it, if a bear comes after us, all I'll have to do is outrun you.'"

The First Liar
Never Has a Chance

Luck, Marv, Eugene, and Salty still had stories to tell after Malcolm finished his. I suspect it was more than just coincidence that left their stories until last. I think each one of them probably held back, waiting to see what the rest of us would come up with. At the same time, I think we were all anxious to go first anyway. It's the old idea about saving the best for last.

After Malcolm's story ended, nobody said anything for a moment or two. Then Luck cleared his throat. "I guess I might as well go next," he said. "I thought I'd tell you about a winter I spent up here with Salty. Actually, I didn't spend the whole winter here. Three years ago, though, I got an idea that it would be educational to come up to see what the weather was like around here in January.

"I flew in right after New Year's and I found out real quick what the weather was like. It was cold, is what it was like. It was so cold if you closed your eyes to blink your eyelashes would freeze together. It was so cold the smell in the outhouse froze solid and plugged both holes. For a couple of days, it was so cold the air all froze and we had to chip it loose with an ice pick so we could breathe.

"Another time, one of my dogs got me up in the night wanting to go outside. After about ten minutes when he didn't come back I figured I'd better go looking for him. As it turned out, he wasn't hard to find. He'd lifted his leg to the first tree he'd come to and was froze right there. I had to chip that ice away, too, so he could get loose and come back inside.

"The next morning, a blizzard came that lasted seven days. When it finally stopped snowing, the wind kept blowing for three more days. In fact, it blew all the snow and ice away and the last two days we had a sand storm.

"The coldest day, though, came afterwards. We were low on food after the blizzard, so I went out to see if I could rustle anything up. I guess I walked about a mile and a half before I came up over a rise in the land and saw a moose just showing his head up over the top of a sand dune.

"I dropped to a crouching position. Apparently, the moose hadn't seen me. I squeezed the trigger and saw fire come out of the gun. But the moose didn't go down. In fact, he just stood there. I was sure I'd made a good shot, but the moose never moved.

I couldn't believe it. I stood up and walked a couple of steps toward the moose. He still didn't move so I fired again. This time, though, as soon as I shot, I saw little cracks start to form all over that moose's body. He just split apart all over the place and fell in a pile.

"Of course, when I saw that, I realized what had happened. That moose had been standing there froze solid in the cold. When I shot him the second time, he just shattered like window glass. The most amazing part, though, was that all that meat broke apart into steaks and roasts and ribs just like on a butcher's chart. When I got it back to the cabin we didn't even have to cut any of it up. We just wrapped it in brown paper and put it in the freezer."

Before I had a chance to wonder who was going to go next, Eugene spoke up. "Years ago," he said, "I used to make duck decoys. Not just any decoys, though. I prided myself on how lifelike I could make 'em. It got so, I s'pose I could have made pretty good money if I'd have gone into the business of duck decoys full time, but it was just a hobby with me. I wasn't doin' it for the money.

"Still, I always tried to do just a little better job each time I made a set of decoys. I'd usually make two ducks at a time and ever' pair I made, I wanted them to be just a little better than the pair before. For the most part, they were, too. I'd figure out some way to improve upon 'em ever' time I'd go to carvin' until finally it got so most folks couldn't tell my ducks from the real birds.

"The last pair I ever made were absolute dandies. After I finished 'em, I took 'em out and sat 'em on the front lawn and just stood there admirin' 'em in the grass. They were beautiful. I'd never seen decoys look so real. Then I got a notion to take their picture and that's how I lost 'em. See, I ran inside to get the camera and, while I was gone, the neighbor's cat come by and caught one of my decoys and ate it. When that happened, it scared my other decoy so bad it flew off and I never saw it again."

I guess everyone expected Marv to go next and he did. Only he waited a moment or two before he started. No one else said anything. Then Marv began telling a story I'd heard before.

It was about one of his trips out west. He said he'd gone out there to camp in the mountains and he backpacked into an incredibly beautiful valley—but it was extremely rugged country. "In fact," he said, "the valley walls were so steep I had to lie down on my back to see the sun come up in the morning. I'd brought my dog along with me, but the valley was so steep he could only wag his tail up and down.

"But it was something that happened on the way up to that valley that I wanted to tell you about. I guess I was most of the way up there when I came across a small flock of bighorn sheep, maybe twenty or thirty of them. Just before I come across them, I'd heard some unusual noises. The first thing I'd heard was just a loud bang or thump. Then it got quiet again, but a minute later, there was another bang.

"When I got to the sheep, though, they were all quiet, grazing there on the side of the mountain. I stopped to look at them for a second, and then I heard another bang. It seemed to be coming from just over the next rise, so I pushed on and there were two, nearly evenly matched rams just a going at it in a life-or-death battle.

"They'd stand way off from each other, you know, maybe a hundred yards or so, and then they'd go to running at each other, put down their heads and whomp, they'd bang their old horns together. And what sets of horns they had. Beautiful. Both pair would have made Boone and Crockett for sure.

"I couldn't believe the punishment they give each other. I must have sat there and watched for an hour and they never let up. They'd come crashing into each other and then turn and run back a hundred yards or so and go at it again. Over and over, they'd bang their heads together so hard you'd think it would have killed them both, but it didn't. They just kept at it.

"After a while, though, I figured I didn't have time to stand and watch them any longer. I had to get on up the mountain. I'd heard about this valley and I wanted to get to it so I could set up camp before dark. As I hiked on, though, I could still hear these two rams banging their heads together, fighting in the only way rams have to fight.

"I wasn't sure, but during the night, I thought I could still hear those rams going at it back there on the mountain. The next morning, I didn't hear anything, but after breakfast I walked back down the trail to see if I could find any evidence of which one of them might have won. They'd seemed to be such an even match I wanted to find out whatever it was about the winner that could make any difference in the outcome.

"When I got there, though, I couldn't believe what I saw. There they both were, still going at it. Only, sometime during the night, both pair of horns had been knocked, or maybe worn, right off their heads. It didn't stop them rams, though. They were still fighting, charging each other from a hundred yards off. But now they were going at it bare-fisted, so to speak.

"I watched them for a good half hour and they never let up. I figured it was only a matter of time, though, before they killed each other, so I went on back to camp. That night, just before dark, I went back and checked on them again, and do you know, they were still going at it. Only now, they'd wore all the hair off their head and I could see where both of them were bleeding a little bit on the top of their scalps.

"I went to bed that night feeling sad, such beautiful animals stubbornly killing each other like that. The next morning, when I woke up, I just packed up and hiked farther up the mountain. I wanted to get somewhere farther away. I wanted to get away from more than just civilization, I wanted to get away from those rams, too.

"I was up on that mountain for two weeks. Most of that time I camped near the peak, just above the tree line, so I could look down and see for miles. I could look across other mountains and valleys all the way to the horizon, probably hundreds of miles away. It was an incredible place, one of the most peaceful times of my life.

"When it came time to go home, I'd pretty well forgotten about those two rams. When I got to the spot I'd seen them fighting, though, I looked up and there were two white clumps of fluff floating in the air. They were about a hundred yards apart, but all at once they went flying towards each other. I couldn't believe it. There was nothing left of those rams but their tails, and the darn fools were still fighting."

It was Salty's turn now. Everyone was quiet. He leaned over and spit tobacco juice into the can at his feet. Afterwards, he took a couple of big, open-mouth chews from his Copenhagen can. Then he looked across the table at Marv, squinting the way he always did when he talked.

"A good many years back," he said, "back before I come up here, or before I went to trapping down in Manitoba, or running a hunting lodge down in Montana, I took a spell where I wanted to see what the country was like farther west. I spent about six years just tramping around through the mountains, even down into some of them river valleys all the way to the Percific Ocean.

"I fixed myself up like a real mountain man. I dressed in buckskins and I even carried an old muzzle-loading rifle everywhere I went. Just lived in the woods. One day, after I'd only been out in that country about six months, I was sitting on a rock eating a peach when a grizzly bear and two cubs come out in the clearing just below me. The old mother grizzly looked up at me, caught a whiff of my scent, and come on right towards me.

"Now, I'll tell you the truth, muzzle-loading rifle or not, right at that time I didn't care for the idea of having a run-in with a mama grizzly with two cubs, so I skedaddled it right off that rock and on up the mountain. The bear, she come after me for a ways, but then just let me go.

"I guess it was about then I recollected that I'd left my little pouch of shooting lead back on the rock. I still had the peach I'd been eating with me, but I'd forgotten the lead. I didn't think it was worth troubling a grizzly bear over, though, so I just kept a hoofing it for more agreeable territorials.

"I was a long way from my main camp at that point. I'd been away exploring the countryside for about a week, which put me near a hundred miles away. There was nothing to do, though, except trudge on back to this little cabin I'd built.

As I walked, I finished eating the peach and then come up with an idea. I stopped and tapped some powder into my rifle. Then I loaded it up with the peach pit. I knew it wasn't much, but that way I figured if another bear come along I would at least have some protection.

"As it turned out, I never saw another bear that trip, but part way home, I got a little hungry, so I started keeping a watch out for game. Before long, of course, I spotted a young buck, so I crept up on it figuring to get close enough to kill it with my peach stone.

"I snuck up without disturbing him, close enough to where I figured he was in range. Then I pulled my old rifle around and fired, aiming for a spot just behind his shoulder. I thought I saw the deer flinch, too, but he never went down. He bounded away through the trees and I was out of luck. I tried tracking him for a while, but I never found even a trace of blood. I figured I must have missed even though I'd been less than a hundred feet from him when I shot.

"After that, I didn't bother trying to make do with that rifle. I just hiked the rest of the way home. And I didn't get back over the mountain into that valley where the deer and the bear were for four or five years. In fact, I'd forgot all about that deer until I saw him again one day. He was easy enough to recognize, too.

"I'd gone back over into that valley to take one last look at it before I headed home to Montana. I'd already got me the idea of opening up a hunting lodge. I'd quit using the old muzzle-loader by then and I was mostly just enjoying the scenery. Along towards the end of the first week on the trail, I camped up under a rock cliff at the edge of the valley.

"The next morning, I woke up early and decided to make my way farther west, down towards the river. The sun had only just started to come up, though, so the trail was dark when I got out there. After a few minutes I decided to lie down under a tree and wait for better light. But I couldn't help myself; the first thing you know, I fell asleep.

"I'm not sure how long I slept, but when I woke up the sun was well high in the sky. The little spot of moss under the tree I was lying against was warm against my head. And I looked up and saw peaches growing in that tree. Honest to carnation, it looked just like heaven.

"But I had to go and spoil everything by reaching up to pull a peach off one of them branches. See, the trouble was that when I did that, why all at once the tree and the ground under it began to move. At first I thought we were having an earthshake, but it weren't. The tree just jumped up and ran off.

"I thought I'd gone daffi-dillies, but then I shook myself off and looked in the direction the tree had run. And I'll be whiskered, but there was a great big buck deer with a full-grown peach tree growing out of its right shoulder. That's when I remembered shooting my peach pit at that young deer a few years before. I should have known I would never have missed him at that range. I'm just too good a shot for that to have happened."

Epilogue

And that's how we came to have our liars contest, and how Salty's yarn about the deer and the peach tree ended it, and how I came to collect enough stories to come home here and write this book. We all said Salty won the contest, although Marv maintained that his story was the best. He said that Salty just had a better way of telling his.

Even after the contest, though, it seemed like we hadn't quite talked ourselves out. As it got dark, the wind continued to blow and the rain to fall. Eugene told a tale about a cyclone that sucked the woodstove in his kitchen up the chimney and blew it "clean away." He said the next day, the same wind came back for the griddles. A few days later, another cyclone picked up a set of wagon tracks in Arkansas and put them back down in Tennessee.

That reminded Salty of a story about a man with a beard so long that when the wind blew from behind him his whiskers would arrive an hour before he did. Marv told about a wind so strong it blew the cribbing out of his well. He said it didn't really matter to him because the darn well hole was so crooked he'd fallen out three times before he finished digging it. Marv said that another time he had a sack of corn hanging on his chicken house door when a whirl-wind came along and blew the sack away, but left the corn still hanging there.

Luck said he'd been in a terrible strong wind one time. He said a politician came along with his mouth open and the wind blew him inside out. A tick opened his mouth in the same wind and it blew him up to the size of a snapping turtle.

There were a few other stories, too, but I'd filled my notebook by that time so I couldn't write them down. I figured I'd get another notebook in the morning, but of course, I forgot the stories by that time. I think I've already mentioned about my memory.

Most everybody turned in before too long anyway. We had to be out on the lake early the next morning to catch some fish. After I went to bed, I lay there awake for a long time thinking about all the stories that had been told. I could hear Salty and Denny still sitting at the table in the common room, talking and telling more tales. "I tell you what, Dennis," I heard Salty say once, "the wind that day cut through to our characters."

Another time, I heard him describe someone as so tall "he couldn't tell when his feet were cold." Salty said the same fellow had to get a stepladder to shave. "He was so skinny," Salty said, "he could walk in the rain and not get wet. Six rattlesnakes struck at him at the same time and every one of them missed."

In the morning, when I woke up, Salty had already left. Denny said that he'd gone back to his cabin farther up Breezy River. Up by Basin Creek and Caribou Lake. The weather had changed over night just the way Salty said it would. The sky was blue, with just stray whisps of cirrus clouds—mare's tails we used to call them. Clouds like that are supposed to be a sign of wind, but there was only a pleasant breeze coming in off the water.

Luck flew back to Timberline Lodge right after breakfast. Everybody else went fishing. I guess Marv and I must have caught two dozen good lakers that day and a lot more of them before the week was out. None of us caught one as big as Malcolm's thirty-pounder, although everybody caught at least a couple that went twenty-five pounds and Marv caught one that weighed twenty-nine.

The last day we were there, I had a huge fish on my line. It was gigantic. I know it's the old story about the one that got away, but you should have seen it. It was the biggest fish I ever saw. I'll bet it weighed at least fifty pounds. It reminds me of the time up on Williams Lake. . . . But then, I guess that's another story. I can write about that another time. Right now, I'm going to go outside again and stretch out for a spell under that walnut tree.

ABOUT THE AUTHOR

Ted Stone is a writer and storyteller currently living on Salt Spring Island in British Columbia. He is the editor of *13 Canadian Ghost Stories* and the author of *The Ghost of Peppermint Flats and Other Stories,* a collection of ghost stories for children. In *The One That Got Away* he returns to the tradition of his two popular books of tall tales, *It's Hardly Worth Talkin' If You're Goin' to Tell the Truth* and *Hailstorms and Hoopsnakes,* which was short-listed for the 1984 Stephen Leacock Humour Award. (By the way, the lake trout in the photograph weighs thirty pounds and was caught by the author at Tree Line Lodge.)